D1045287

THE MICROSTRUCTURE OF METALS

THE MICROSTRUCTURE
OF METALS

J. NUTTING, M.A., B.Sc., Ph.D., F.I.M.

Professor of Metallurgy
Houldsworth School of Applied Science
The University, Leeds

and

R. G. BAKER, M.A., Ph.D., A.I.M.

Chief Metallurgist (Ferrous)
British Welding Research Association
Abington Hall, Cambridge

Institute of Metals
Monograph and Report Series
No. 30

1965
THE INSTITUTE OF METALS
17 Belgrave Square, London, S.W.1

First published 1965

© THE INSTITUTE OF METALS
1965

*Printed in Great Britain by Richard Clay (The Chaucer Press), Ltd.,
Bungay, Suffolk*

CONTENTS

Contents

PREFACE

THE aim in producing this volume has been to provide a collection of annotated micrographs which would be of assistance to students of metallurgy. It is hoped that the collection will be useful in the teaching of practical metallography and, in addition, will provide the background of metallographic evidence for the teaching of a variety of topics in physical metallurgy.

During the last few years there have been revolutionary changes in metallography. These have been brought about by the introduction of the electron microscope and the electron-probe microanalyser, and by the development of the extraction-replica and thinfoil transmission techniques which have allowed the electron microscope to be used to the limit of its capabilities in the examination of metals. Electron micrographs are used to illustrate specific features such as dislocations and the structural changes found during the early stages of the decomposition of supersaturated solid solutions, for in these cases the optical micrographs are almost without meaning. Micrographs obtained with the scanning microprobe analyser have been included to illustrate the changes in composition introduced during the oxidation of metals.

While it is realized that many students, even up to honours degree standard, will not get the opportunity of using an electron microscope or an electron-microprobe analyser, the authors feel that all students of metallurgy should be aware of the basic metallurgical structures which can be revealed with these instruments. It is their hope that the juxtaposition of optical and electron micrographs, where the underlying aim has been to choose the technique best fitted to illustrate the required features, will help students, and perhaps their tutors, to appreciate the power of metallographic methods.

Wherever possible, the micrographs should be studied in relation to the appropriate equilibrium diagrams. But to have included all these diagrams in the present volume would have been impractical and is almost unnecessary, since so many good sources of the diagrams are available. The nomenclature of the phases given in the text and captions corresponds to that used in the Annotated Equilibrium Diagrams published by the Institute of Metals. Where compositions are given these are all in weight per cent. unless otherwise stated.

One hundred years have elapsed since H. C. Sorby first developed techniques for the examination of metals with the optical microscope. During this period, the microscope and metallographic methods have played an ever-increasing role in the development of the scientific study of metals. At the same time, the metallurgist's approach to the investigation of the relationships between structure and mechanical properties is finding an increasing application to non-metallic materials, such as organic polymers and ceramics. However, a few metallographic problems still remain to be solved, such as those associated with the structure of solid solutions, the nature of grain boundaries, and solute segregation to boundaries and other structural defects.

The present volume may be looked upon, then, as a summary of one hundred years of metallographic development and the authors take great pleasure in dedicating it to the memory of H. C. Sorby.

J. NUTTING
R. G. BAKER

Acknowledgements

THE production of this monograph was originally suggested by the Metal Physics Committee of the Institute, and Dr. H. J. Axon and one of the present authors (J.N.) were asked to provide a draft outline. This was approved and a sub-committee was formed to advise on the details of preparation. Subsequently, the present authors were invited to assemble and edit the micrographs. They wish to thank Dr. H. J. Axon and the members of the sub-committee for their advice and comments, particularly during the early stages of collecting the micrographs and the writing of the first few chapters.

Metallographers in a variety of industries, research associations, and universities were approached and asked to submit micrographs from their files. Although the field of interest was outlined wherever possible, no specific requirements were mentioned. As a result, about twelve hundred micrographs were collected and an attempt was then made to fit these into the previously established framework of the monograph. The authors would like to thank most sincerely all those who so readily responded to the request; their names are appended below. Because of limitations of space and content the finished volume contains only one quarter of the micrographs submitted and the authors would like to apologize to those metallographers who find that some of their cherished specimens have not been reproduced. It is only to be hoped that they will approve of the choice which has been made.

Dr. A. J. Baker, United States Steel Corporation.

Mr. J. Barlow, The G.K.N. Research Laboratories.

Mr. K. P. Bentley, British Welding Research Association.

Dr. A. Berghezan, European Research Associates, Brussels.

Mr. R. E. Berry, Manganese Bronze, Ltd.

M. Hervé Bibring, Office National d'Etudes et de Recherches Aéronautiques, France.

Dr. T. Boniszewski, British Welding Research Association.

Dr. C. J. L. Booker, The National Chemical Laboratory.

Dr. I. A. Brammar, Aeon Laboratories.

Dr. D. Brandon, Metallurgy Department, University of Cambridge.

Miss E. D. Brown, British Welding Research Association.

Dr. J. C. Chaston, Johnson, Matthey and Co., Ltd.

Dr. J. Christian, Department of Metallurgy, University of Oxford.

Dr. J. Coiley, Aeon Laboratories.

Mr. G. Clough, Deva Metal Co.

Miss M. K. B. Day, British Aluminium Co., Ltd.

Mr. R. Eborall, British Non-Ferrous Metals Research Association.

Dr. V. W. Eldred, United Kingdom Atomic Energy Authority, Reactor Group.

Professor E. C. Ellwood, formerly of the Tin Research Institute.

Dr. E. F. Emley, Magnesium Elektron, Ltd.

Dr. R. M. Fisher, United States Steel Corporation.

Dr. P. G. Forrester, Glacier Metal Co., Ltd.

Professor G. A. Geach, formerly of Associated Electrical Industries, Ltd.

Mr. W. Gifkins, British Welding Research Association.

Mr. W. L. Grube, General Motors Corporation, U.S.A.

Mr. D. M. Haddrill, British Welding Research Association.

Mrs. J. Y. Halnan, Production Tool Alloy, Ltd.

Dr. D. R. Harries, United Kingdom Atomic Energy Authority, Harwell.

Dr. J. G. Hines, Agricultural Division, I.C.I., Ltd.

Dr. P. B. Hirsch, Cavendish Laboratory, Cambridge.

Professor R. W. K. Honeycombe, Department of Metallurgy, University of Sheffield.

Mr. I. C. H. Hughes, British Cast Iron Research Association.

Dr. T. Hurlen, Sentral Institutt for Industriell Forskning, Blindern, Norway.

Dr. E. D. Hyam, United Kingdom Atomic Energy Authority, Reactor Group.

Mr. T. James, Enfield Rolling Mills, Ltd.

Dr. J. M. Jepson, United Kingdom Atomic Energy Authority.

Mr. G. T. Kay, G.K.N. Research Laboratories.

Dr. P. M. Kelly, Department of Metallurgy, University of Leeds.

Professor P. Lacombe, Centre de Recherches Métallurgiques de l'Ecole Supérieure des Mines de Paris, France.

Dr. P. H. R. Lane, Drop Forging Research Association.

Dr. D. McLean, The National Physical Laboratory.

Dr. J. May, United Kingdom Atomic Energy Authority, Harwell.

Mr. E. Mitchell, Joseph Lucas, Ltd.

Dr. I. Mitchell, International Nickel, Ltd.

Dr. S. W. K. Morgan, Imperial Smelting Corporation, Ltd.

Mr. R. P. Newman, British Welding Research Association.

Dr. R. B. Nicholson, Metallurgy Department, University of Cambridge.

Dr. W. Nixon, Department of Engineering, University of Cambridge.

Dr. M. J. Olney, Gillette Research Laboratories.

Dr. D. Pashley, Tube Investments Research Laboratories.

Mr. H. W. L. Phillips, formerly of British Aluminium Co., Ltd.

Mr. F. B. Pickering, United Steel Companies, Ltd.

Dr. T. Ll. Richards, formerly of Metals Division, I.C.I., Ltd.

D. K. Sachs, G.K.N. Research Laboratories.

Dr. A. Schrader, Max-Planck-Institut für Eisenforschung, Düsseldorf, Germany.

Mr. A. A. Smith, British Welding Research Association.

Professor C. S. Smith, formerly Institute for the Study of Metals, Chicago, U.S.A.

Dr. E. Smith, Associated Electrical Industries, Ltd.

Mr. G. C. Smith, Metallurgy Department, University of Cambridge.

Dr. P. R. Swann, United States Steel Corporation.

Dr. D. Lloyd Thomas, Department of Metallurgy, Imperial College of Science and Technology, London.

Professor G. Thomas, Metallurgy Department, University of California, U.S.A.

Dr. J. R. Vilella, United States Steel Corporation.

Mr. R. H. Wade, Cavendish Laboratory, Cambridge.

Mr. F. Watkinson, British Welding Research Association.

Dr. A. A. Wells, British Welding Research Association.

Professor W. C. Winegard, University of Toronto, Canada.

Dr. G. C. Wood, Chemical Engineering Department, Manchester College of Science and Technology.

Mr. R. N. Younger, Davy-Ashmore, Ltd.

The following proprietary alloys are mentioned in the text:

Alcomax III (Permanent Magnet Association); Armco iron (American Rolling Mill Co.); Magnox (Magnesium Elektron, Ltd.); Nicrosilal (Sheepbridge Stokes Centrifugal Castings Co., Ltd.); Ni-hard (International Nickel Co., Inc.); Nimonic (Henry Wiggin and Co., Ltd.); Ni-resist (Ferranti Ltd.); Permalloy (Standard Telephones and Cables Ltd.); SAP(Swiss Aluminium, Ltd.).

SECTION I. FUNDAMENTAL METALLOGRAPHY

CHAPTER 1

The Structure of Pure Metals and Single-Phase Alloys

SOLID metals may be prepared by crystallization from a liquid, by condensation from a vapour, or by deposition from solution. In each case characteristic microstructures are obtained. The most important mode is by crystallization from the melt. The structures and properties of the solid metal so obtained depend upon the alloy content and the solidification conditions.

In most alloys the equilibrium diagram at low solute concentrations is as shown in Fig. 1.A. On cooling the liquid of composition C_0, solid of composition C_s is formed at the temperature T_s. As the solid is purer than the liquid at the solid /liquid interface, the liquid becomes enriched with solute. A steady-state distribution of solute is eventually set up in the liquid when the concentration of solute in the freezing solid is equal to the original solute concentration C_0 (Fig. 1.B).

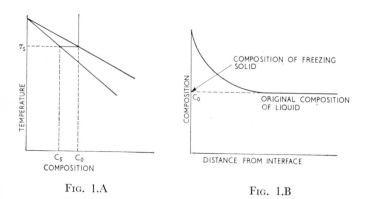

FIG. 1.A   FIG. 1.B

The temperature at which solidification will occur under equilibrium conditions in the liquid ahead of the interface rises to the value T_s as the liquid composition approaches C_0. The correspond-

1

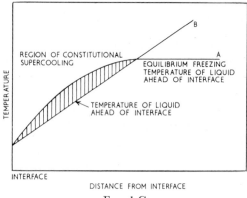

FIG. 1.C

ing equilibrium freezing temperature of the enriched liquid ahead of the interface is shown in curve A, Fig. 1.C.

As heat is being abstracted during solidification, a temperature gradient is developed in the liquid (curve B, Fig. 1.C). Under the conditions shown, the liquid in the shaded region is below its equilibrium freezing temperature and is said to be constitutionally supercooled. The amount of supercooling is increased by raising the solute content, by increasing the rate of solidification (R), or by decreasing the temperature gradient in the liquid (G). For a given solute content the solidification structures produced depend upon the value of the ratio G/R; i.e. upon the amount of constitutional supercooling.

The structures developed during the solidification of a metal may be removed by reheating to high temperatures and this process may be accelerated if the metal is hot or cold worked. Recrystallization then occurs, to give grains having a characteristic polygonal shape.

The ideal shape of the individual grains is a tetrakaidecahedron, a solid figure having eight hexagonal faces and six square faces. Such grains fit together and completely fill space. In practice, this ideal shape is not attained. The angle of misorientation between neighbouring grains is relatively large; thus the grain boundaries are regions of considerable atomic misfit and consequently are of high energy. The grain boundaries are easily delineated, therefore, by etching a polished metal specimen. The structure revealed is a series of polygons resulting from the random section which has been made through the polyhedral grains. Each grain is generally sub-divided further into smaller sub-grains. The orientation difference across a sub-grain boundary is usually $< 1°$; therefore sub-grain boundaries are of lower energy than grain boundaries and consequently are not as easy to delineate by etching techniques.

PLATE I

Figures 1.1–1.3

FIG. 1.1. Zinc cast into the form of a cylindrical ingot and then sectioned transversely. Etched in 5% hydrochloric acid. Small equiaxed grains have been formed at the periphery of the ingot as a result of the rapid chilling by the cold mould wall. Columnar crystals have then grown inwards to the centre of the ingot. × $\frac{1}{2}$.

FIG. 1.2. Nickel pellet produced by the decomposition of nickel carbonyl at a temperature of 180° C. Sectioned through a diametral plane and etched in a mixture of nitric and acetic acids. The structure is very fine grained and the successive layers of decomposition are shown as a series of concentric circles. × 5.

FIG. 1.3. Chromium deposited electrolytically at a temperature of 45° C from a solution of chromium trioxide in dilute sulphuric acid. Direct examination of the deposited surface shows a network of fine cracks intersecting at ∼90°. Such a crack network arises as a result of the internal stresses generated during electrodeposition. × 500.

PLATE I 5

1.1

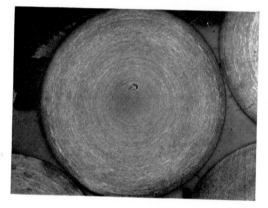

1.2

1.3

B

PLATE II

Figures 1.4–1.7

This series illustrates the influence of purity and rate of casting upon the macrostructure of continuously cast aluminium ingots. In each case a longitudinal section has been prepared and then etched in Tucker's reagent. $\times \frac{1}{2}$.

FIG. 1.4. Aluminium 99·9% pure, poured at 700° C into a mould to give a casting rate of 6 in./min. Large columnar grains extend across the specimen.

FIG. 1.5. Aluminium 99·8% pure, poured at 700° C into a mould to give a casting rate of 6 in./min. Equiaxed grains have formed against the mould wall and columnar grains then extend inwards to the centre.

FIG. 1.6. Aluminium 99·5% pure, poured at 700° C into a mould to give a casting rate of 6 in./min. With a greater impurity content, equiaxed crystals form more easily and the columnar grains are much finer.

FIG. 1.7. Aluminium 99·2% pure, poured at 680° C into a mould to give a casting rate of 8 in./min. With the greater impurity content and increased casting rate, the columnar grains are no longer formed.

PLATE II   7

1.4   1.5   1.6   1.7

PLATE III

Figures 1.8–1.13

This series illustrates the transition in growth substructures resulting from impurity enrichment ahead of an advancing solid/liquid interface and the subsequent constitutional supercooling in tin containing 0·006 at.-% lead. The specimens were prepared by allowing partial solidification to occur and then decanting the remaining liquid. Micrographs were obtained from the direct examination of the untreated solid/liquid interface. The micrographs show the substructures within the advancing columnar grains. × 50.

FIG. 1.8. Sample grown at a G/R ratio of 2000 degC/cm²/sec (R = growth rate (cm/sec), G = temperature gradient in liquid (degC/cm)). Under these growth conditions, a plane interface with no impurity substructure is found. A grain boundary runs diagonally across the micrograph.

FIG. 1.9. Sample grown at a G/R ratio of 2000 degC/cm²/sec. Under these growth conditions, a pock-marked interface occurs.

FIG. 1.10. Sample grown at a G/R ratio of 1000 degC/cm²/sec. Under these conditions, elongated cells are formed.

FIG. 1.11. Sample grown at a G/R ratio of 400 degC/cm²/sec. Under these conditions, the cells have changed from an elongated to an hexagonal shape.

FIG. 1.12. Sample grown at a G/R ratio of 350 degC/cm²/sec. The cells are now all hexagonal in cross-section.

FIG. 1.13. A specimen similar to those shown in Figs. 1.8–1.12 but containing 0·2 at.-% lead and grown at a G/R ratio of 200 degC/cm²/sec. Under these conditions, side branching occurs to give the characteristic dendritic structure. To obtain the structure, low G/R ratios are necessary, the actual value depending upon the impurity content. For an alloy content of 0·006 at.-% lead, an extremely low G/R ratio (∼30) would be necessary to ensure a dendritic structure.

PLATE III   9

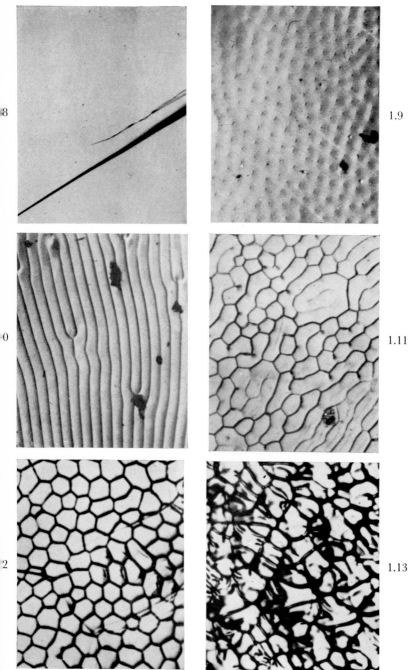

PLATE IV

Figures 1.14–1.17

FIG. 1.14. Copper containing 7% nickel and 3% aluminium, chill cast into an ingot of 2 in. dia. Etched in 10% ammonium persulphate. The microstructure shows cored dendrites, the darker regions being the richer in copper. × 50.

FIG. 1.15. Same specimen as in Fig. 1.14 but hot forged to 1 in. dia. after casting. Recrystallization has occurred to give equiaxed grains containing many growth twins. However, coring still persists to a slight extent. × 100.

FIG. 1.16. Pure aluminium in the wrought condition. Electropolished and anodized in sulphuric acid. On examination under polarized light, the polygonal grain structure is clearly revealed. × 50.

FIG. 1.17. Brass, containing 50% copper and 50% zinc (β), lightly cold worked and then exposed to ammonia vapour. With this treatment, preferential attack occurs at the grain boundaries and the metal falls apart to give individual grains. The grain shape approximates to a tetrakaidecahedron and individual facets having four, five, and six edges may be seen. × 75.

PLATE IV 11

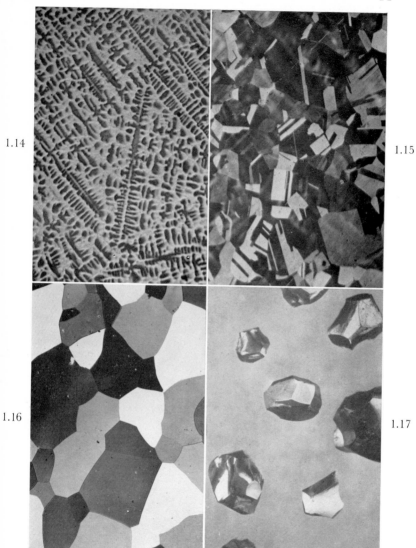

1.14

1.15

1.16

1.17

PLATE V

Figures 1.18 (*a*) and (*b*)

FIG. 1.18 (*a*) and (*b*). Aluminium containing 5% tin. Specimen prepared as a foil 1 mm thick and examined in the X-ray microscope by transmission.

Tin is only very slightly soluble in aluminium and, on heating above 230° C, the tin has formed a liquid film around the aluminium grains. On examination by X-rays, the tin-rich regions appear dark owing to absorption. This enables the polyhedral grain structure of the aluminium to be observed within a bulk specimen. The micrographs should be viewed by turning through 90°. Stereographic pair × 100.

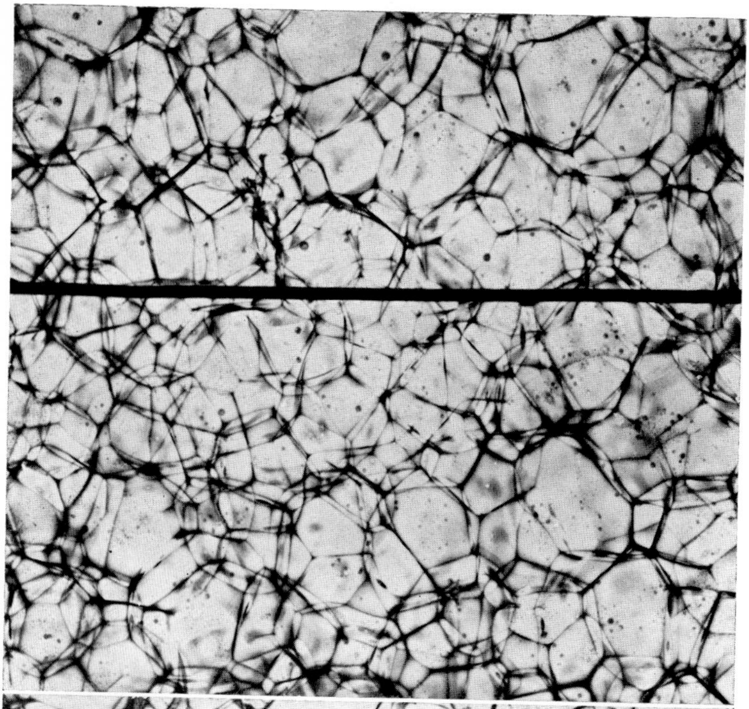

PLATE V

1.18
(*a*)

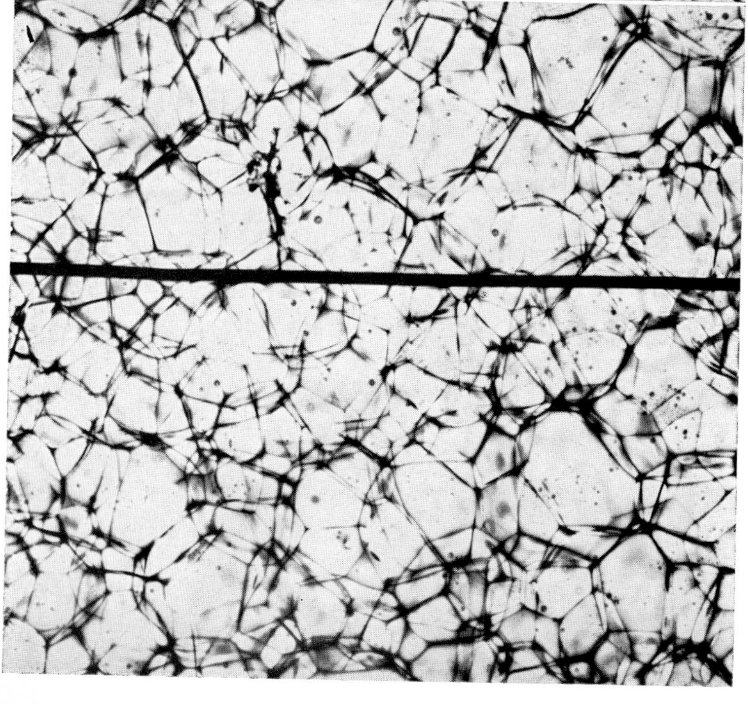

1.18
(*b*)

PLATE VI

Figures 1.19–1.21

FIG. 1.19. Pure aluminium in the wrought condition.   Electropolished and
etched in Lacombe's reagent.
  Etch pits have been formed within the grains and the faces of the
pits are parallel to {100} planes of the aluminium lattice.   Therefore
the differences in pit profile are indicative of the changes in grain
orientation.   × 100.

FIG. 1.20. Pure aluminium, lightly cold worked and then annealed.
Etched in Lacombe's reagent.
  Within the large grains, subgrains are visible.   (*a*) Bright-field and
(*b*) dark-field illumination.   × 1.

FIG. 1.21. Pure aluminium, lightly cold worked and then reheated below
the recrystallization temperature.   Etched in Lacombe and Beau-
jard's reagent.
  Preferential etch-pit formation has occurred at the sub-grain boundaries.   × 100.

PLATE VI   15

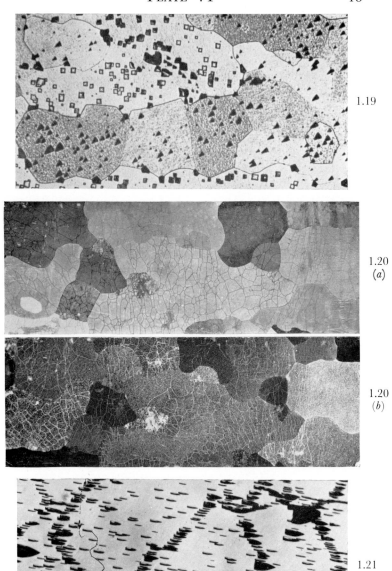

1.19

1.20
(a)

1.20
(b)

1.21

CHAPTER 2

The Microstructural Changes across the Equilibrium
Diagrams of Binary Alloys

THE equilibrium diagram of any binary mixture can be regarded as a combination of simple units. The microstructural types usually associated with these units are cellular structures, cored dendrites, eutectics, and peritectics, all of which arise from liquid → solid reactions, and eutectoids and peritectoids which arise from reactions completely in the solid state. When complete miscibility in both the liquid and solid state occurs, the microstructures conform to one of the types described in Chapter 1.

A common equilibrium unit is a simple eutectic and an example of this is found in the lead–tin system, which shows a eutectic formed from a lead-rich phase containing tin in solid solution and a tin-rich phase containing lead in solid solution, as shown in Fig. 2.A.

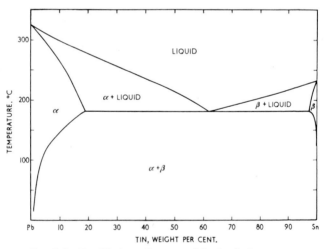

FIG. 2.A. Equilibrium diagram of the lead–tin system.

When lead is added to pure molten tin it is completely miscible but, on cooling, dendrites of a tin-rich solid solution form first and the remaining liquid becomes gradually richer in lead. The dendrites continue to grow until the liquid reaches the eutectic composition (63% Sn, 37% Pb), when a mixture of the tin-rich and

16

lead-rich phases is deposited. If the lead content exceeds 37%, then the primary phase will be lead-rich solid solution. In this case the primary dendrites grow and the liquid becomes progressively richer in tin until the eutectic composition is reached once more. Eutectics can also be formed between intermetallic compounds and primary solid solutions, but intermetallics may also appear as isolated particles without forming part of any recognizable eutectic structure.

The eutectoid reaction resembles a eutectic reaction, except that it occurs entirely in the solid state. The most important example of a eutectoid reaction is that found in steels when austenite decomposes at 723° C to give pearlite, a eutectoid mixture of ferrite and cementite. This is illustrated in Chapter 16 (p. 120).

A peritectic reaction occurs in the copper–zinc system, where the α phase (face-centred cubic solid solution of zinc in copper) reacts with liquid to give the β phase, a body-centred cubic solid solution of zinc in copper. Peritectoid reactions may be complex, as shown by the example found in the copper–aluminium system.

When two-phase alloys are heated, the shape of the second-phase particles will depend upon the interfacial energy between the dispersed and matrix phases. If the interfacial energy is high, the dispersed phase will tend to form spheres, whereas if the interfacial energy is low the particles tend to form films along the grain boundaries.

PLATE VII

Figures 2.1–2.6

FIG. 2.1. Pure tin. Etched in 2% hydrochloric acid in alcohol. The contrast between the grains is due to differences in their orientation. A substructure has been revealed within the more heavily attacked grains. × 75.

FIG. 2.2. 90% tin–10% lead. Etched in 1 part acetic acid + 1 part nitric acid + 8 parts glycerol. The light-etching phase is the tin-rich solid solution in a dendritic form and the eutectic forms an in-filling. × 75.

FIG. 2.3. 70% tin–30% lead. Etched as in Fig. 2.2. The dendritic form of the primary tin-rich phase is readily apparent, while the amount of eutectic has increased. × 75.

FIG. 2.4. 63% tin–37% lead. Etched as in Fig. 2.2. The structure is now entirely eutectic. The light-etching phase is tin-rich and the dark-etching phase is lead-rich. × 75.

FIG. 2.5. 40% tin–60% lead. Etched in 1 part nitric acid + 3 parts acetic acid + 5 parts glycerol. Shows dark-etching dendrites of the lead-rich phase surrounded by eutectic. × 75.

FIG. 2.6. Pure lead. Chemically polished and etched in 1 part hydrogen peroxide + 3 parts acetic acid. In this case the etchant attacks the grain boundaries and little grain-contrast etching has occurred. × 75.

PLATE VII

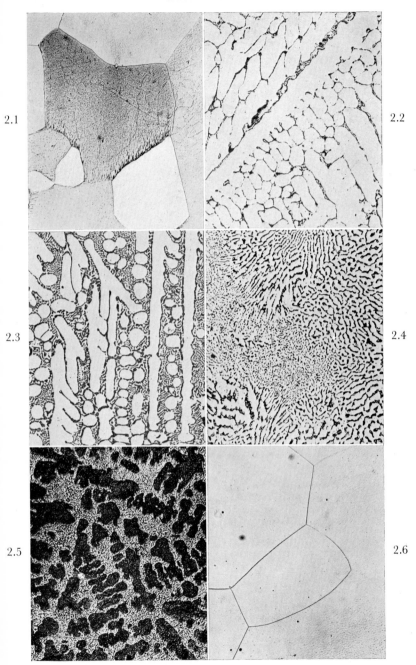

2.1

2.2

2.3

2.4

2.5

2.6

The Microstructure of Metals

PLATE VIII

Figures 2.7–2.9

FIG. 2.7. Copper–8% phosphorus in the as-cast condition. Unetched. The light areas are primary copper and the eutectic consists of a mixture of copper, containing phosphorus in solid solution, and the intermetallic compound Cu_3P. × 250.

FIG. 2.8. Particles of $FeSn_2$ in tin containing a small amount of iron as an impurity. Unetched. × 1000.

FIG. 2.9. Copper–22% zinc–2% aluminium, in the as-cast condition. Etched in ammonia/hydrogen-peroxide mixture. The primary phase (α) is copper-rich, and at the peritectic temperature the residual liquid reacts with the primary phase to produce the β phase, which is dark-etching. × 250.

PLATE VIII   21

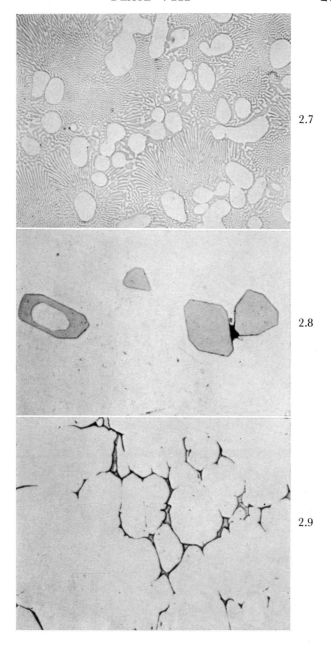

2.7

2.8

2.9

PLATE IX

Figure 2.10

FIG. 2.10. Copper–12·3% aluminium, cooled from 800 to 500° C at a controlled rate and then water-quenched. Electrolytically etched in 1% chromic acid. At 800° C the alloy is all-β (b.c.c.), but, on cooling, the γ_2 phase (complex body-centred cubic) precipitates (see Fig. 2.B). If the cooling rate is sufficiently rapid, the equilibrium eutec-

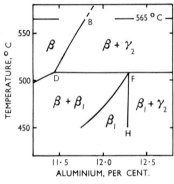

FIG. 2.B

toid reaction of $\beta \rightarrow \alpha$ (f.c.c.) $+ \gamma_2$ is suppressed, and instead a peritectoid reaction occurs between β and γ_2 at 508° C. This gives rise to a new phase β_1, which is richer in aluminium than β and has an ordered structure. The β_1 phase (light-etching) forms as a film around the γ_2 phase (half-tone) as it reacts with β (dark). Small particles of γ_2 may transform completely to β_1 during the reaction. $\times 1000$.

PLATE IX

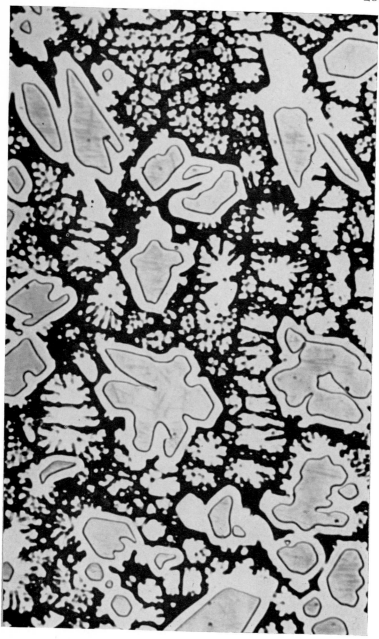

2.10

PLATE X

Figures 2.11–2.13

FIG. 2.11. Copper–16% tin, held at 650° C for 10 h and then water-quenched. The matrix phase is a solid solution of tin in copper (α). The β phase, which is richer in tin, forms at the α grain boundaries. The energy of the α/β interface is almost equal to that of the α/α interface and consequently the β phase does not spread along the α grain boundaries. × 250.

FIG. 2.12. Copper–30% zinc–3% lead, heated at 700° C and then quenched. The dark particles are almost pure lead, and the matrix is the α-brass solid solution of zinc in copper. The lead particles within the grains are spherical. At the grain boundaries the lead particles could be described as triangles with convex sides. This is a result of the energy of the α/Pb interface being greater than that of the α/α interface. × 350.

FIG. 2.13. Copper–1% bismuth, annealed at 800° C. Bismuth is only sparingly soluble in copper and tends to form as a film around the copper grain boundaries. This is because the energy of the Cu/Bi interface is considerably lower than that of the Cu/Cu interface. Within the grains the bismuth still forms spherical particles. × 350.

PLATE X   25

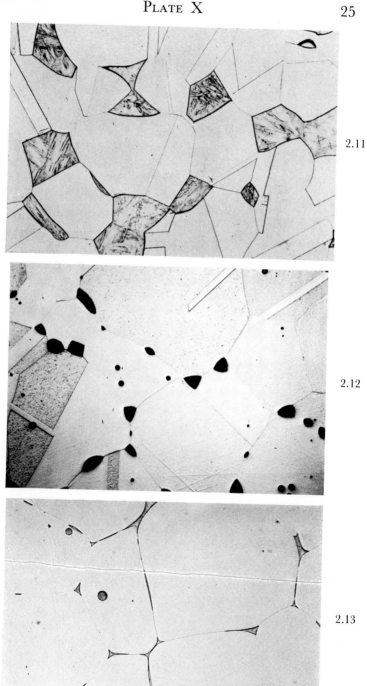

2.11

2.12

2.13

CHAPTER 3

The Deformation of Metals and Alloys in Tension

PLASTIC deformation occurs in metals by the movement of dislocations. Where the dislocations run out at the surface, steps are produced and, by examining the height and orientation of these steps, the mode of deformation may be deduced. The step height may vary from a few Ångström units to a few microns in magnitude and thus, under the optical microscope, the steps often appear as fine lines known as " slip lines ".

Various techniques are available for studying slip lines. Much useful information can be obtained with the conventional light microscope but, where the slip displacements are small, more refined optical techniques such as phase contrast and interferometry may be required. The electron microscope may be used to study replicas of the surface but, although high resolving powers may be obtained parallel to the surface, the replica methods are not very sensitive to small changes in surface height.

If, when dislocations are generated, they move along well-defined slip planes giving displacements in definite directions, straight slip lines are produced. The individual slip displacements are usually independent of the total strain, further deformation being accommodated by the development of new slip lines. In polycrystalline materials or single crystals deformed at high strains, slip occurs on several systems, producing more than one parallel set of slip lines.

In aluminium, the slip lines visible under the optical microscope may be seen in the electron microscope to be bands of many fine lamellæ with a spacing of ~ 200 Å. In this case further strain may be accommodated by the addition of new lamellæ to existing bands. In iron, slip bands are produced but no lamellæ can be resolved and the strain appears to be homogeneous within the band.

Edge dislocations cannot move out of the slip plane except by a diffusion process but screw dislocations may change readily from one slip plane to an intersecting (conjugate) slip plane; this is known as cross-slip. In some metals, large strains give rise to unusual modes of deformation; localized regions of secondary slip may be formed and these are known as kink bands and deformation bands. Within these bands local rotation of the lattice occurs.

At room temperature and low strain rates, cubic metals usually deform by slip. However, at low temperatures or high strain rates, deformation may occur by twinning, giving twin bands in which the deformation is completely homogeneous. Non-cubic metals often deform at room temperature by a combination of slip and twinning, e.g. tin.

Both grain boundaries and precipitates provide obstacles to the movement of dislocations and, as a result, slip lines may change direction at these points of intersection. When the dislocations meet a boundary, they may continue into the neighbouring grain without undue hindrance if the orientation difference between the slip systems is sufficiently small. In general, however, for slip to continue, a stress concentration must be developed sufficient in magnitude to activate dislocation sources in the neighbouring grain. Under these conditions the boundaries are kinked during deformation. When cross-slip can occur, it may be easier for the dislocations to move in a direction parallel to the boundary, giving highly localized strains in this region. The slip lines are now bent as they approach the boundary until they run parallel with it. Deformation of this type frequently results in intercrystalline failure.

The type of interaction between precipitates and dislocations depends upon the nature of the precipitated phase, its size, and its interface with the matrix. With coherent and partially coherent phases, the dislocations may pass through the particles, thus deforming them. With incoherent particles, cross-slip may occur around the particles and wavy slip lines are found. When precipitates are present at grain boundaries, it becomes more difficult for slip to propagate across the boundary, so leading to localized strain near the boundary and eventually to intercrystalline failure.

PLATE XI

Figures 3.1–3.3

FIG. 3.1. Pure iron, electropolished and then plastically deformed 4%. Examined under the optical microscope using normally incident illumination. Under these conditions, no slip markings are visible. × 300.

FIG. 3.2. The same area of the specimen shown in Fig. 3.1 but examined using phase-contrast illumination. The surface distortion as a result of slip is now visible. × 300.

FIG. 3.3. The same area of the specimen shown in Fig. 3.1 but examined using a two-beam interferometric technique to reveal differences in surface height. A plane surface would show a series of parallel bands. × 300.

PLATE XI   29

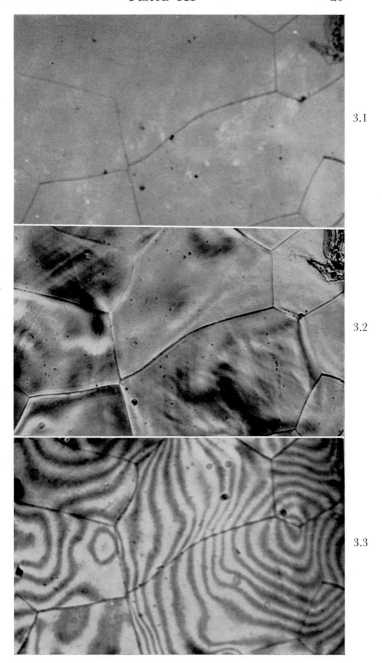

3.1

3.2

3.3

PLATE XII

Figure 3.4

Fɪɢ. 3.4. Stainless steel, electropolished and plastically deformed 10%. The polished surface has been masked with lacquer and the specimen electrochemically thinned from the other side to produce a thin foil, the cross-section of which is wedge-shaped at its edge. The specimen has then been examined by transmission in the electron microscope. The serrations along the edge of the foil represent the slip displacements produced by dislocations which have moved through the grain and have piled up against the grain boundary running diagonally across the micrograph. Electron micrograph. × 45,000.

PLATE XII 31

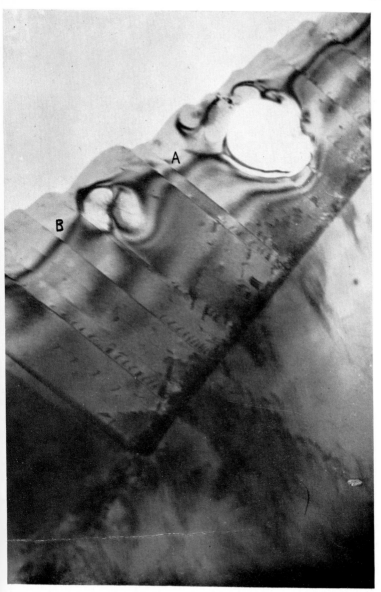

3.4

PLATE XIII

Figures 3.5–3.7

FIG. 3.5. Copper–30% zinc, electropolished and deformed 10% in tension. The surface structure was replicated using silicon monoxide and the replica examined in the electron microscope. Slip has occurred on two systems; the slip lines of the primary system are faulted by slip on the secondary planes. Electron micrograph. × 20,000.

FIG. 3.6. Pure aluminium, electropolished and deformed 80% in tension. An oxide replica was taken from the surface and examined in the electron microscope. Slip has occurred in bands each of which contains fine lamellæ having a separation of 200 Å. Electron micrograph. × 20,000.

FIG. 3.7. Pure aluminium, electropolished and deformed 10%. Slip has occurred in clusters of parallel bands running horizontally across the micrograph. Many of these bands are linked by cross-slip on a conjugate system. × 150.

PLATE XIII   33

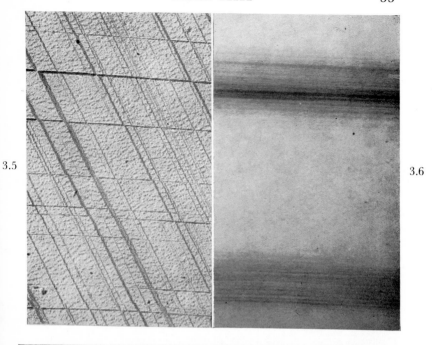

3.5

3.6

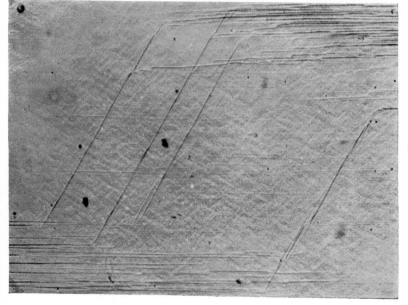

3.7

PLATE XIV

Figures 3.8–3.11

FIG. 3.8. Pure aluminium, electropolished and deformed 17% in tension. The strain is not homogeneous even on a macroscopic scale, since deformation bands have been formed in which secondary slip has occurred. × 70.

FIG. 3.9. Pure aluminium, electropolished and deformed 17·5% in tension. To accommodate the strain, local rotation of the lattice has occurred giving rise to a kink band. The formation of these bands is by a deformation mechanism intermediate between that for slip and that for twinning. × 300.

FIG. 3.10. Pure iron, electropolished and then deformed at −193° C. After 3% strain, fracture occurred and the plastic deformation has been accommodated chiefly by twinning in narrow irregular bands. × 1200.

FIG. 3.11. Pure iron, electropolished and then deformed at −70° C by striking with a hammer. Plastic deformation has occurred by twinning, but the twins formed at a high strain rate are very narrow. They are known as Neumann lamellæ. × 600.

Plate XIV   35

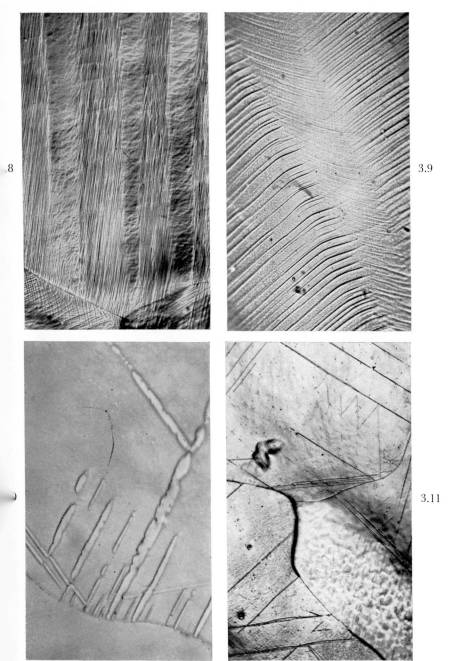

PLATE XV

Figures 3.12–3.14

FIG. 3.12. Pure iron, electropolished and then plastically deformed 30% in tension. The slip bands are wavy and change direction as they approach the grain boundaries. × 150.

FIG. 3.13. Pure iron, plastically deformed to fracture at room temperature. A section was taken near the point of fracture and then polished and etched. The displacements at the grain boundary have occurred by slip passing from one grain to the next. Electron micrograph of carbon replica. × 13,000.

FIG. 3.14. Aluminium–7% magnesium, solution-treated, quenched, and then aged at 150° C for 43 h. After electropolishing, the specimen was deformed 24% in tension. Precipitation of β (Mg_2Al_3) has taken place at the grain boundary to give an almost continuous film. During plastic deformation the dislocations were unable to cross the boundary and have therefore cross-slipped in a direction parallel to the boundary, so giving curved slip lines. Electron micrograph of oxide replica. × 3000.

PLATE XV   37

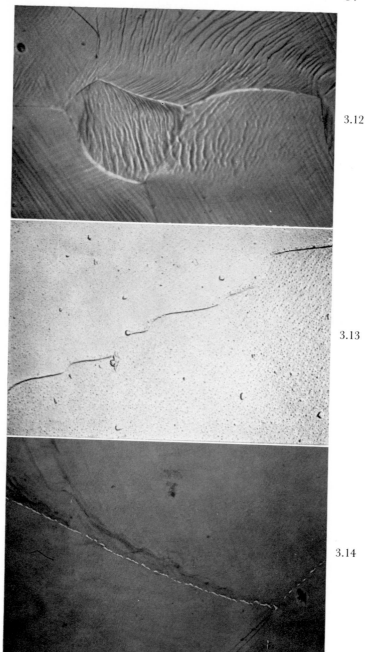

3.12

3.13

3.14

D

PLATE XVI

Figures 3.15 and 3.16

FIG. 3.15. Aluminium–4% copper, solution-treated, quenched, and then aged at 320° C for 20 h. After electropolishing, the specimen was deformed 28% in tension. During ageing, the θ' phase $CuAl_2$ has precipitated as partially coherent Widmanstätten plates along the {100} matrix planes. During plastic deformation, the dislocations pass through the plates, so deforming them. Electron micrograph of oxide replica. × 17,000.

FIG. 3.16. Aluminium–4% copper, solution-treated, quenched, and aged at 320° C for 100 h. After electropolishing, the specimen was deformed 40% in tension. During ageing, the equilibrium phase ($CuAl_2$) has been formed as spherical particles which are completely incoherent with the matrix. On deforming, the dislocations find it easier to cross-slip around rather than to pass through the particles; therefore wavy slip lines are produced. Electron micrograph of oxide replica. × 15,000

PLATE XVI 39

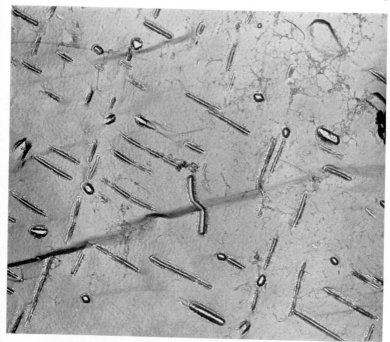

3.15

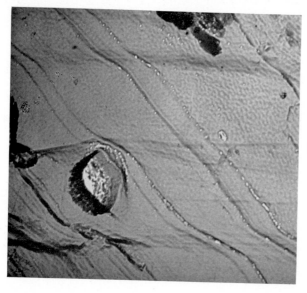

3.16

CHAPTER 4

Deformation by Creep and Fatigue

WHEN a metal is deformed at high temperatures the slip-line pattern differs from that found at low temperatures. At high temperatures progressive deformation may occur at constant load, over long periods of time. This phenomenon is known as creep. In the early stages of creep deformation, the strain rate is high and straight slip lines are produced. The rate of deformation at first decreases with time, until a steady state is reached. The slip lines then become wavy and eventually sub-grains are formed. Deformation may also occur by grain-boundary migration and grain-boundary sliding. Eventually, the creep rate increases and at this stage voids are found at the grain boundaries.

When metals are subject to cyclical stressing, failure may ultimately take place at stresses well below those required for failure in a tensile test. This phenomenon is known as fatigue. Highly localized strain occurs in bands of closely spaced slip lines. Cracks form within these bands and propagate across the grains and sometimes around the grain boundaries, until the stresses acting on the uncracked metal become so high that rapid failure takes place. The fracture surface shows striations which indicate the progress of the fracture during each stress reversal.

Fatigue failure may occur in non-cubic metals without the application of external stress. During thermal cycling, anisotropic expansion and contraction can lead to the development of stresses large enough ultimately to cause fatigue failure.

PLATE XVII

Figures 4.1–4.3

FIG. 4.1. Pure aluminium, electropolished then deformed in creep at 0·5 ton/in² at 200° C for 25 h to give 3·4% extension. The slip lines that develop are mainly straight. × 50.

FIG. 4.2. Pure aluminium, electropolished then deformed in creep at 0·5 ton/in² at 200° C for 696 h to give 16% extension. The slip lines have now become very irregular. × 50.

FIG. 4.3. Pure aluminium, electropolished then deformed in creep at 0·75 ton/in² at 200° C for 118 h to give 29·5% extension. After deforming, the surface was anodized and examined with polarized light. A sub-grain structure has developed within the grains. × 50.

PLATE XVII 41

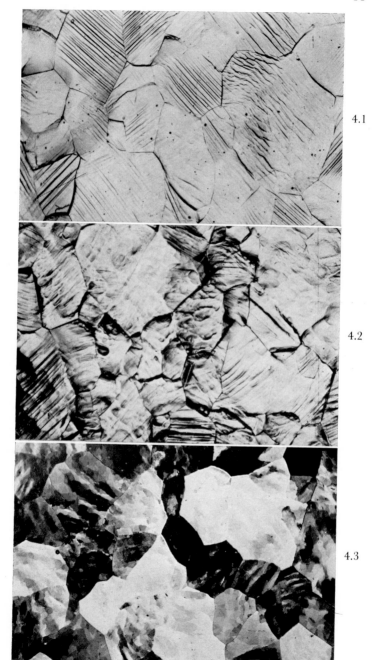

4.1

4.2

4.3

PLATE XVIII

Figures 4.4–4.7

FIG. 4.4. Pure aluminium, electropolished then deformed in creep at 0·5 ton/in² at 200° C for 179 h to give 12% extension. Grain-boundary migration has occurred under the action of the applied stress. × 50.

FIG. 4.5. Pure aluminium, electropolished then marked with a scratch. Deformed by creep at 0·5 ton/in² at 200° C for 179 h to give 12% extension.

During deformation, grain-boundary sliding has occurred, giving rise to displacement of the scratch as it crosses the boundaries. × 50.

FIG. 4.6. Nimonic 90 (Cr 20, Co 15, Fe 5, Si 1·5, Ti 7, Al 1·5, Mo 1·0, C 0·1%, balance nickel), deformed in creep at 2½ tons/in² at 900° C for 1900 h to give 8½% extension. Sectioned after deforming and etched in 50% aqua regia, 50% glycerol. Bead-like grain-boundary voids have formed which are typical of creep deformation at low stresses. × 500.

FIG. 4.7. Same alloy as Fig. 4.6, deformed in creep at 8 tons/in² at 800° C for 2739 h to give 7% extension. Sectioned after deforming and etched in 50% aqua regia, 50% glycerol. A wedge-shaped crack has formed, running along a grain boundary from a grain corner. This behaviour is typical of creep deformation at high stresses. × 500.

PLATE XVIII 43

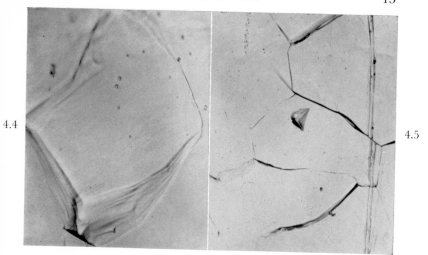

4.4

4.5

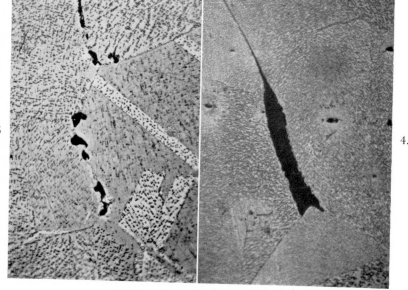

.6

4.7

Figures 4.8–4.10

FIG. 4.8. Aluminium–1% magnesium, electropolished and then fatigued at a high strain to 50% of its expected life. Broad slip bands have been produced from which fatigue cracks can develop.   × 250.

FIG. 4.9. Same area of specimen as Fig. 4.8 after light electropolishing. The slip steps produced by fatigue in the lower grain have been removed entirely by the polishing treatment, but in the upper grain the fatigue deformation was more severe and cracks were present along the slip bands which were not removed by electropolishing.   × 250.

FIG. 4.10. Same area of specimen as Fig. 4.9, but now fatigued to fracture. Slip steps have again been produced in the lower grain and are present in the upper grain in exactly the same position as in Fig. 4.8.   × 250.

PLATE XIX

45

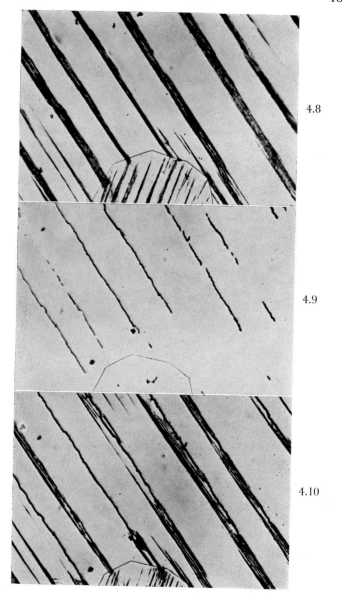

4.8

4.9

4.10

PLATE XX

Figures 4.11–4.13

FIG. 4.11. Stainless steel (18%Cr, 8%Ni), electropolished and fatigued for 5% of life. The polished surface has been masked with lacquer and the specimen electrochemically thinned from the other side to produce a thin foil, the cross-section of which is wedge-shaped at the edge. The specimen was then examined by transmission in the electron microscope. The striations represent the displacements produced by slip during the fatiguing and a crack is developing along the slip band. The arrow indicates the direction of maximum taper magnification. Electron micrograph. × 40,000.

FIG. 4.12. Aluminium–4%copper, in the solution-treated condition electropolished and then fatigued at a stress of ±4 tons/in² for 50,000 cycles. In localized regions, metal has been extruded along the slip bands. × 400.

FIG. 4.13. Aluminium–7% zinc–3% magnesium, solution-treated, quenched, aged, and put into service, where failure occurred as a result of fatigue. Carbon replica was prepared from the fracture surface and examined in the electron microscope. The concentric striations indicate the progress of the fatigue fracture. Each striation corresponds to one stress reversal. Electron micrograph. × 1000.

PLATE XX   47

4.11

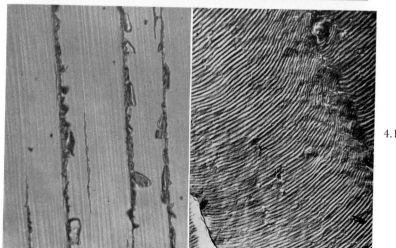

.12   4.13

PLATE XXI

Figures 4.14–4.16

FIG. 4.14. Pure cadmium, electropolished and then thermally cycled 20 times between 30 and 100° C. As the thermal expansion is anisotropic, stresses are generated during heating and cooling and these have led to plastic deformation.   × 100.

FIG. 4.15. Pure cadmium, electropolished and then thermally cycled 20 times between 30 and 150° C.   × 100.

FIG. 4.16. Pure cadmium, electropolished and then thermally cycled 20 times between 30 and 250° C.   The greater the temperature difference in the thermal-cycling treatment, the more severe are the stresses. Ultimately fatigue failure will occur in a manner analogous to that in mechanical fatigue.   × 100.

PLATE XXI 49

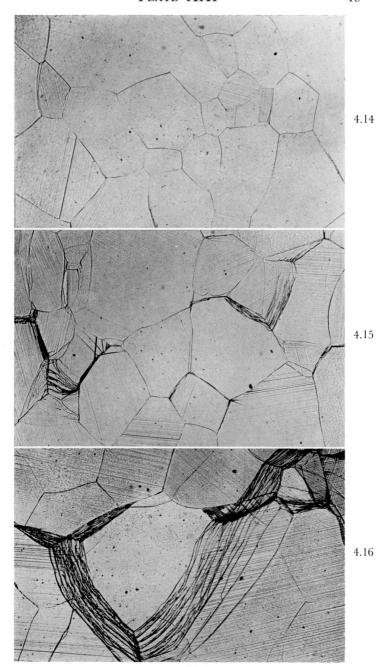

4.14

4.15

4.16

CHAPTER 5

Dislocations and Stacking Faults

On examining metal foils 200–1000 Å thick by transmission in the electron microscope it is possible to observe lattice defects directly. The elastic strain field surrounding a dislocation (a line defect) causes the electrons to be diffracted from that region; thus the image shows a dark line indicative of the position of the dislocation within the foil. On cold working a metal, the dislocation density is increased and, on reheating, the dislocations migrate to form networks. In face-centred cubic metals, a dislocation may dissociate into two partial dislocations separated by a stacking fault (a plane defect), in which the sequence of planes corresponds to a thin layer of an hexagonal structure. Diffraction effects produced by the lattice displacements enable the stacking faults to be observed in the electron microscope. Vacant lattice sites (point defects) cannot be observed directly in the electron microscope. However, if a metal is heated close to its melting point and then quenched it may become supersaturated with respect to vacancies, and these excess vacancies can precipitate in various forms to give structures visible with the aid of the electron microscope.

PLATE XXII

Figures 5.1–5.4

FIG. 5.1. Armco iron, deformed 4% and thinned by electropolishing. Examined in the electron microscope by direct transmission. The dislocations are roughly parallel to each other in this region and, as the slip direction is also nearly parallel to the dislocation lines, they probably have a predominantly screw character. Electron micrograph. × 80,000.

FIG. 5.2. Armco iron, deformed 10% and thinned by electropolishing. Examined in the electron microscope by direct transmission. As deformation takes place, the dislocations on different slip systems interact to give complicated tangled networks. These impede further slip causing the metal to become harder. Electron micrograph. × 80,000.

FIG. 5.3. Armco iron, deformed 10% then annealed at 700° C, and thinned by electropolishing. Examined in the electron microscope by direct transmission. On annealing the cold-worked iron, the dislocations tend to form regular networks from the irregular tangles. These networks may be regarded as sub-boundaries within the grains. Electron micrograph. × 80,000.

FIG. 5.4. Stainless steel (18% Cr, 8% Ni), deformed 2% and then thinned by electropolishing. Examined in the electron microscope by direct transmission. A group of stacking faults lie along one slip plane. Each stacking fault is bounded by two partial dislocations which pass through the foil. The striations are perpendicular to the partials and run parallel to the foil surface. Electron micrograph. × 60,000.

PLATE XXII   53

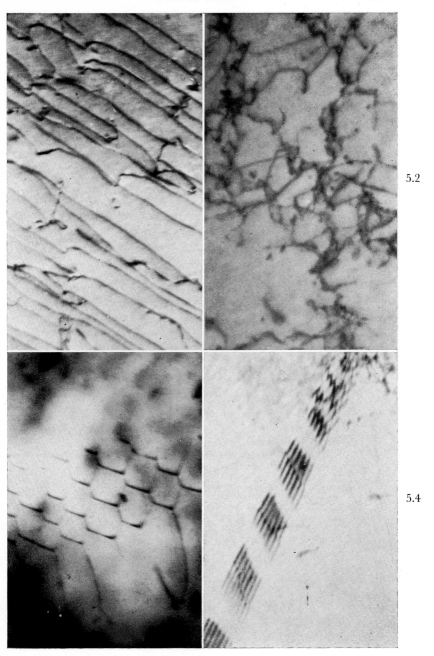

5.2

5.4

E

PLATE XXIII

Figures 5.5–5.8

Fɪɢ. 5.5. Copper–8% aluminium, deformed at −196° C and thinned by electropolishing. Examined in the electron microscope by direct transmission. Dislocations have formed piled-up groups against a twin boundary. Electron micrograph. × 10,000.

Fɪɢ. 5.6. Pure aluminium, quenched from 600° C and thinned by electropolishing. Examined in the electron microscope by direct transmission. Vacancies formed in the metal at the high temperature are precipitated as discs on quenching. When the discs exceed a critical size they collapse, leaving dislocation loops at their perimeters. × 20,000.

Fɪɢ. 5.7. Aluminium–4% copper, quenched from 540° C and thinned by electropolishing. Examined in the electron microscope by direct transmission. When this alloy is quenched, some loops are formed, but vacancies may also " condense " on dislocations. In the case of screw dislocations this results in the dislocation assuming a spiral configuration, as shown in the micrograph. × 40,000.

Fɪɢ. 5.8. Aluminium–4% copper, aged at 200° C for 200 h and deformed 1%. Thinned by electropolishing and examined in the electron microscope by direct transmission. Dislocations of different Burgers vectors are cutting through precipitates of the θ' (CuAl$_2$) phase. × 20,000.

PLATE XXIII   55

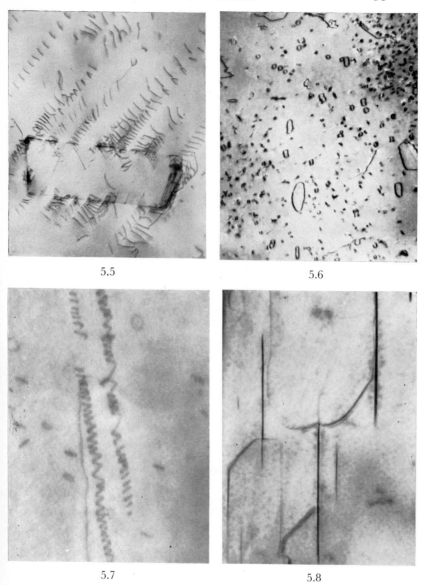

5.5   5.6

5.7   5.8

CHAPTER 6

Pure Metals and Alloys Cold-Worked and Annealed

WHEN a polycrystalline metal is cold rolled, the grains undergo elongation in the direction of flow. Ultimately, it becomes impossible to determine the grain shape under the light microscope. On annealing cold-worked materials recrystallization occurs, a process that involves the nucleation of new grains which grow in an equiaxed way. With large amounts of prior cold deformation, the recrystallized grains usually have a preferred orientation. The grain size obtained and the degree of preferred orientation depend chiefly on the amount of cold work and the annealing conditions.

PLATE XXIV

Figures 6.1–6.4

This series of photomicrographs illustrates the effect of progressively increasing rolling reductions on the structure of 70 : 30 brass. Specimens were etched in ammonia and hydrogen peroxide.

The micrographs are longitudinal sections with the rolling direction parallel to the long axis of the photograph. They show the change of grain shape accompanying the deformation, with a complete loss of identity of the boundaries after 90% deformation. × 150.

FIG. 6.1. Annealed strip.

FIG. 6.2. Cold-rolled 40%.

FIG. 6.3. Cold-rolled 70%.

FIG. 6.4. Cold-rolled 90%.

PLATE XXIV   57

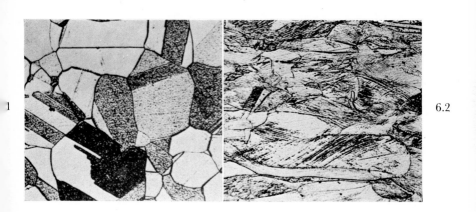

1

6.2

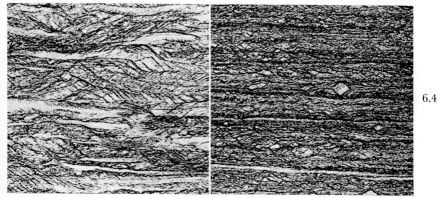

6.4

PLATE XXV

Figures 6.5–6.8

This series of photomicrographs illustrates the effect of final rolling reduction on the development of cube texture after annealing high-conductivity copper strip. Specimens had an initial grain size of 0·04 mm and the final annealing temperature was 900° C. Specimens were etched in ammonia and hydrogen peroxide, followed by electrolytic staining.

The specimens were sectioned parallel to the strip surface and the rolling direction is parallel to the short axis of the photograph. In the cube texture the (001) planes lie parallel to the strip surface, with the [100] directions parallel to the rolling direction. The rate of chemical attack is lowest on {100} planes; thus, as the preferred orientation develops, the amount of grain contrast shown on etching decreases.   × 100.

FIG. 6.5. 80% reduction

FIG. 6.6. 90% reduction

FIG. 6.7. 95% reduction

FIG. 6.8. 97% reduction

PLATE XXV   59

6.5

6.6

6.7

6.8

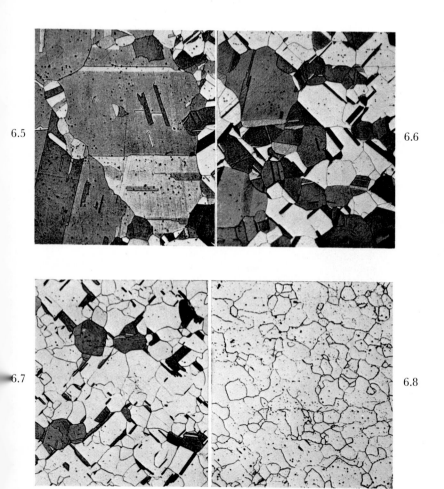

PLATE XXVI

Figure 6.9

FIG. 6.9. A series of specimens illustrating the effect of prior cold work on the subsequent grain size after annealing. Specimens of commercial aluminium were subjected to 2, 6, 8, and 10% deformation, and then heated up to 600° C in $1\frac{1}{2}$ h and water-quenched. Etched in $12\frac{1}{2}$% sodium hydroxide, followed by a macro-etch in a mixture of nitric, hydrochloric, and hydrofluoric acids. The progressive decrease in grain size with increasing amounts of prior cold work is clearly shown. × 1.

PLATE XXVI   61

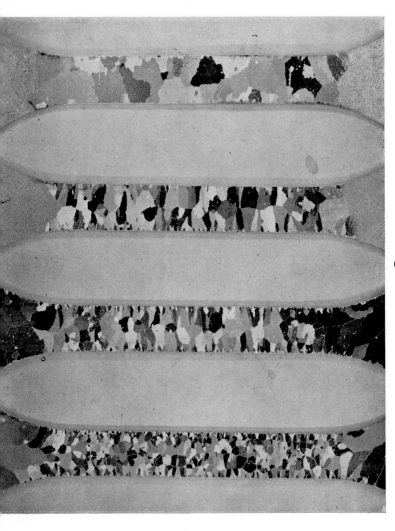

6.9

Chapter 7

Phase Changes in the Solid State

Phase changes in the solid state can occur in two ways: by a process involving nucleation and a diffusion-controlled growth, or by a diffusionless shear, i.e. a martensitic transformation. Occasionally, both processes may contribute to the reaction, as in the formation of bainite.

When a phase change takes place at a high temperature or a low cooling rate, nucleation can occur only at very favourable sites, such as grain boundaries. At lower transformation temperatures, or with rapid cooling rates, nucleation may take place within the grains of the unstable phase, leading to the formation of a Widmanstätten structure. In alloy systems where the solid solubility decreases with decreasing temperature, a supersaturated solid solution may be produced on cooling rapidly.

On reheating, the supersaturated solid solution decomposes and the change from the metastable to the stable condition occurs via a sequence of intermediate metastable states. The usual sequence is: zones of high solute concentration, intermediate precipitates fully coherent with the matrix, partially coherent intermediate precipitates, incoherent stable precipitates. The approach to equilibrium occurs by the route that gives the greatest rate of change of free energy, i.e. the reaction follows the easiest path rather than the shortest. This sequence may be modified at the grain boundaries and by heating the supersaturated solution at high temperatures close to the solvus, when the equilibrium phase may be nucleated directly. In a multicomponent supersaturated solution, the sequence of precipitated phases depends upon the concentrations and rates of diffusion of the various components; as a result many metastable phases may form before the equilibrium phase appears.

In some alloy systems, a phase stable only at a high temperature cannot be preserved by rapid cooling to a low temperature. The stable phase transforms on cooling via a diffusionless shear transformation to give a new metastable phase. Such reactions occur during the transformation of austenite to martensite, during the allotropic change of cobalt from the face-centred cubic to the hexagonal form, and during the decomposition of the β phase in the titanium–aluminium system.

Internal oxidation is a special case of a nucleation-and-growth type change, where one of the components, oxygen, diffuses through the matrix to react with the solute to produce an insoluble compound.

Order–disorder transformations also proceed by nucleation and growth and it is possible to observe the growth of ordered domains with the aid of the microscope.

PLATE XXVII

Figures 7.1–7.3

FIG. 7.1. 0·2% Carbon steel, heated to 1200° C and air-cooled. Etched in 2% nital. A large austenite grain size has been established at the high temperatures and, on cooling, ferrite is precipitated initially at the austenite boundaries, but as the degree of supercooling increases nucleation occurs within the austenite grains themselves giving rise to a Widmanstätten precipitate. The carbon-enriched austenite has subsequently transformed to fine pearlite, unresolved at this magnification. × 200.

FIG. 7.2. Aluminium–4% copper, heated to 540° C and water-quenched, then aged for 16 h at 130° C. Thin foil prepared by electropolishing and examined by transmission in the electron microscope. The Guinier–Preston zones have been formed as plates parallel to the {100} planes of the face-centred cubic matrix and at this stage are in the form of a single layer of copper atoms ∼100 Å in dia. In view of the 10% difference in atomic diameter between aluminium and copper, plate-like growth of the zones is favoured. Only the plates lying in one crystallographic orientation are visible. Electron micrograph. × 1,000,000.

FIG. 7.3. Aluminium–16% silver, solution-treated at 520° C and water-quenched, then aged for 5 days at 160° C. Thin foil prepared by electropolishing, examined by transmission in the electron microscope. Spherical zones rich in silver are formed ∼100 Å in dia. As the atomic diameters of silver and aluminium are almost identical, the zones can grow radially without developing large strains. Electron micrograph. × 200,000.

PLATE XXVII 65

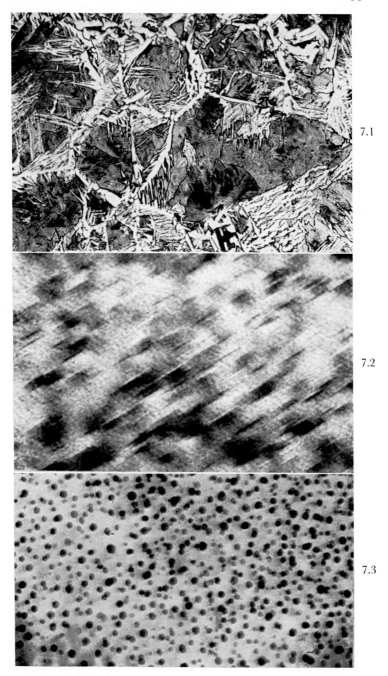

7.1

7.2

7.3

PLATE XXVIII

Figures 7.4–7.6

FIG. 7.4. Aluminium–4%copper, solution-treated at 540° C, quenched in water, and aged for 1 day at 130° C. Thin foil prepared by electropolishing, examined by transmission in the electron microscope. With further ageing the zones shown in Fig. 7.2. change to give the θ'' phase, which is a metastable intermediate precipitate having a unit cell different from that of the matrix. The matrix and precipitate are coherent and this leads to a strain field being developed in the matrix around the precipitates. This strain field may be observed as a dark region surrounding many of the precipitates. Electron micrograph. × 800,000.

FIG. 7.5. Aluminium–4% copper, solution-treated at 540° C, quenched in water, and aged for 3 days at 200° C. Thin film prepared by electropolishing, examined by transmission in the electron microscope. On further ageing, the θ'' phase transforms to another intermediate metastable phase θ'. During this transformation, the precipitated particles grow considerably and lose coherency with the matrix. The strain fields disappear. Electron micrograph. × 25,000.

FIG. 7.6. Aluminium–16%silver, solution-treated at 520° C, water-quenched, and aged for 100 days at 160° C. Thin film prepared by electrolytic polishing, examined by transmission in the electron microscope. During further ageing of this alloy, the metastable γ' phase forms as plates on the $\{111\}$ planes of the matrix, while the zones (shown in Fig. 7.3) go back into solution. × 8000.

PLATE XXVIII 67

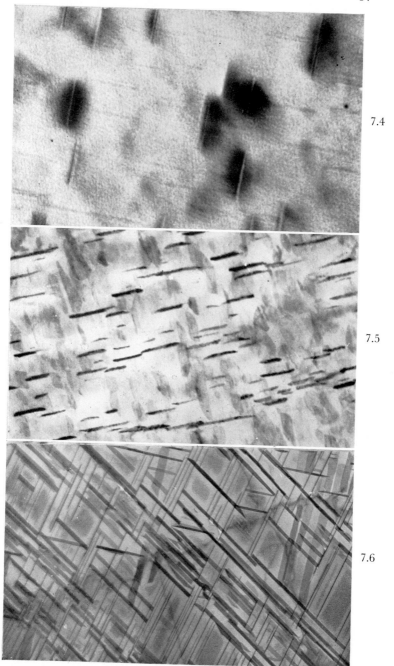

7.4

7.5

7.6

PLATE XXIX

Figures 7.7–7.10

Fig. 7.7. Aluminium–4% copper, solution-treated at 540° C, water-quenched, and aged for 12 h at 200° C. Thin film, prepared by electropolishing and examined by transmission in the electron microscope. On preferential sites, such as grain boundaries and spiral dislocations, the θ' phase may be precipitated directly, denuding the surrounding matrix of copper. There is also a general background precipitate of fine particles of θ'', which are, however, not resolved at this low magnification. Electron micrograph. × 3000.

Fig. 7.8. Iron–0·013% carbon, solution-treated at 710° C, brine-quenched, and aged for 10 min at 260° C. Carbon-extraction replica examined in the electron microscope. Cementite precipitates initially on dislocations. As the precipitates grow, strains are developed which give rise to dislocation loops around the particles so providing sites for further precipitation. In this way a dendritic form of precipitate results. Electron micrograph. × 25,000.

Fig. 7.9. Aluminium–7·5% zinc–2·5% magnesium, solution-treated at 520° C, water-quenched, and aged for 20 days at 160° C. Thin film prepared by electropolishing and examined by transmission in the electron microscope. Within the grains there is a Widmanstätten precipitation of M'-MgZn$_2$ on the {111} planes. Spheroidal precipitates have formed on the grain boundary and there is a precipitate-free region on each side of the boundary. The M' particles adjacent to this region are larger than those in the body of the grain. Electron micrograph. × 15,000.

Fig. 7.10. Iron–0·02% carbon heated at 700° C for 1 h, water-quenched and then tempered at 200° C for 15 h. Cementite has precipitated preferentially on the sub-grain boundaries. × 1000.

PLATE XXIX 69

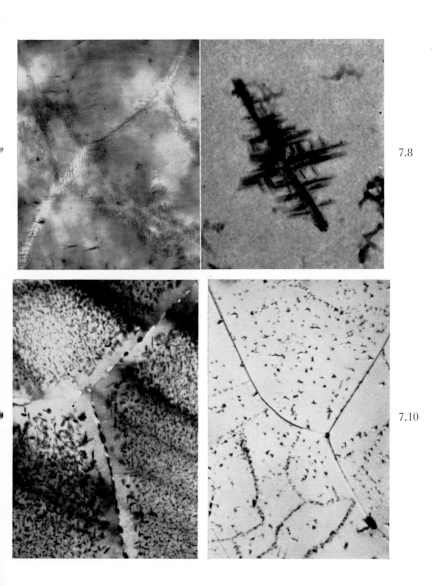

7.8

7.10

The Microstructure of Metals

PLATE XXX

Figures 7.11 and 7.12

FIG. 7.11. Steel (3% Cr), austenitized at 1050° C, rapidly cooled to 700° C, and isothermally transformed at this temperature for 35 min, then water-quenched. After heat-treatment, the carbides were isolated by anodic dissolution of the ferritic matrix. The extract was collected and examined in the electron microscope.

During isothermal transformation, the first carbide phase to precipitate is cementite. However, cementite is metastable in the presence of chromium at these temperatures and $(Fe,Cr)_7C_3$ is nucleated within the cementite plates. As the $(Fe,Cr)_7C_3$ grows, the cementite plates dissolve, leaving " windows " as shown in the micrograph. Electron micrograph. × 22,000.

FIG. 7.12. Steel (1% Cr, 0·5% Mo, 0·5% V) austenitized at 930° C, air-cooled, and tempered for 1 h at 700° C, then creep tested for 3588 h at 550° C. The precipitating phases were extracted in a plastic-extraction replica. The square plate-like precipitates are V_4C_3 and these provide sites where the more stable M_6C carbide may be nucleated in the form of needle-shaped particles. Electron micrograph. × 80,000.

PLATE XXX

71

7.11

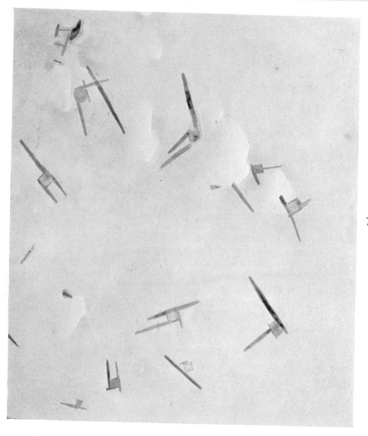

7.12

PLATE XXXI

Figures 7.13–7.16

FIG. 7.13. Pure cobalt, polished and then heated to 530° C under vacuum. Examined at the elevated temperature. At room temperature, cobalt has an hexagonal structure, which changes allotropically to a face-centred cubic structure by a shear transformation. The micrograph shows traces parallel to the $(111)_{fcc}$ $(0002)_{hex}$ planes which appear on the surface of the earlier hexagonal grain structure as the transformation takes place. × 25.

FIG. 7.14. Titanium–10%aluminium, heated to 1200° C and water-quenched. Etched in $1\frac{1}{2}\%$ hydrofluoric acid with 3% nitric acid in aqueous solution. At the high temperature, the alloy is body-centred cubic (β) but, on cooling rapidly, it transforms by a shear transformation to give the close-packed hexagonal structure (α), which has an acicular form. × 100.

FIG. 7.15. Copper–1% aluminium, heated at 950° C for 3 h in Cu_2O. Thin foil prepared by electropolishing and then examined by transmission in the electron microscope. During heat-treatment, oxygen diffuses through the copper and combines with the aluminium to produce small alumina particles. The band running diagonally across the micrograph is a twin and within this region the strain fields around the particles may be observed. Electron micrograph. × 90,000.

FIG. 7.16. Gold–50% copper, prepared as a thin foil by vacuum evaporation. The sample was then heated between 380 and 410° C and rapidly cooled. With this treatment a superlattice CuAu(II) is formed. The ordered structure consists of long narrow domains, the boundaries of which give contrast in the electron microscope. Electron micrograph. × 360,000.

PLATE XXXI 73

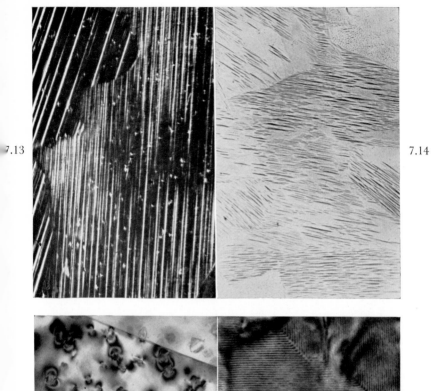

7.13

7.14

15

7.16

SECTION II. COMMERCIAL NON-FERROUS ALLOYS

CHAPTER 8

Brasses

COPPER has a face-centred cubic structure and is capable of dissolving up to 38% of zinc in substitutional solid solution, so forming the α-brasses. Further additions of zinc lead to the formation of the β phase containing ∼ 50% zinc, which has a body-centred cubic structure. The γ phase has a complex body-centred cubic structure and contains ∼ 58% zinc. The commercial alloys are usually either all-α or mixtures of (α + β) phases.

The all-α alloys will withstand severe cold deformation and are widely used as tubing and as sheet for deep drawing and pressing. The β phase is soft at high temperatures and becomes hard on cooling. The (α + β) alloys are commonly hot worked at a temperature at which they consist predominantly of the β phase. They may be extruded or hot stamped. Cast brasses are usually of the (α + β) type and often contain minor additions of aluminium, iron (for grain refinement), and other elements to improve the properties without changing the general structure.

Two characteristic modes of failure of the brasses are season-cracking and dezincification. Season-cracking is a form of stress-corrosion cracking and is found when the cold-worked alloys, containing internal stresses, are exposed to a corrosive environment, particularly one containing ammonia. Dezincification may result from solution in a corrosive environment, followed by reprecipitation of porous copper at the same site.

PLATE XXXII

Figures 8.1–8.3

FIG. 8.1 Copper–30%zinc, cold worked, annealed at 850° C, and air-cooled. Electropolished and lightly etched in aqueous ferric chloride. Equiaxed grains of α-brass showing many annealing twins characteristic of copper alloys. The grain orientation greatly influences the rate of attack during etching and this effect is particularly noticeable across a twin boundary. × 400.

FIG. 8.2. Copper–40%zinc, chill cast in the form of ½-in.-dia. ingot. Mechanically polished and etched in ferric chloride. Widmanstätten precipitation of α (white) in a matrix of β (dark). Precipitation of α has also occurred at the β grain boundaries. × 105.

FIG. 8.3. Copper–40% zinc, chill cast as above and then annealed at just below the α/β phase boundary. Prepared as specimen 8.2. Showing spheroidized grains of α (white) in a matrix of β (dark). × 150.

PLATE XXXII 75

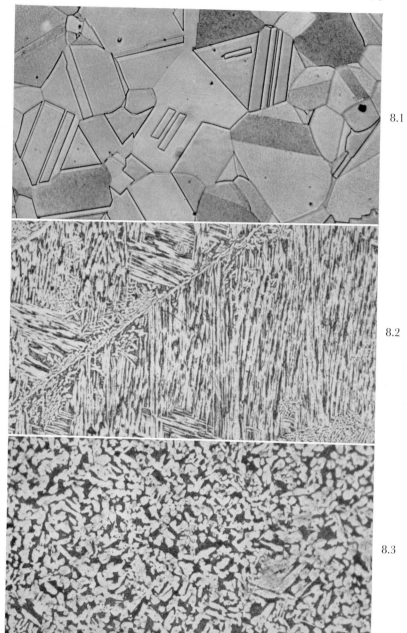

8.1

8.2

8.3

PLATE XXXIII

Figures 8.4–8.6

FIG. 8.4. Copper–40% zinc, cast and then hot rolled, finishing at 450° C, i.e. within the two-phase region. Mechanically polished and etched in ammonium persulphate. Elongated grains of α and β phases are visible; the α grains are more deeply etched and show twins. × 250.

FIG. 8.5. Copper–52% zinc, in cast condition. Etched in sodium dichromate. The γ phase is dark-etching and is situated both at the boundaries and within the β grains. × 150.

FIG. 8.6. Copper–39·5% zinc–0·5% lead, chill cast, reheated into the β range and extruded into bar. Etched in acidified alcoholic ferric chloride. Shows the α phase in a matrix of β, with a uniform distribution of small lead particles. × 100.

PLATE XXXIII 77

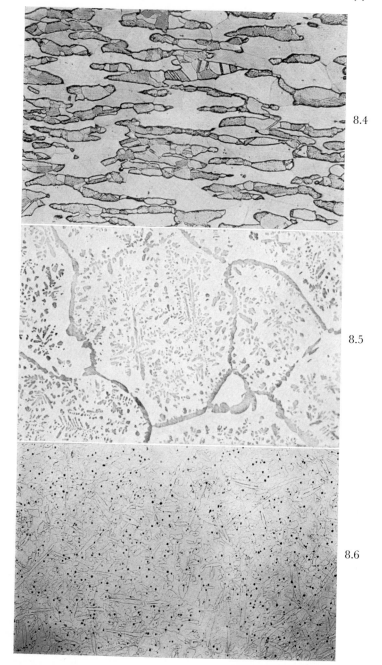

8.4

8.5

8.6

PLATE XXXIV

Figures 8.7 and 8.8

FIG. 8.7. Copper–30% zinc, cast, annealed, cold drawn, and then exposed to an atmosphere containing ammonia. Electropolished and etched in ammonium persulphate. Shows twinned α grains with an inter-crystalline crack (season-cracking). × 75.

FIG. 8.8. Copper–40% zinc, extruded into bar and then held in a corrosive environment. Etched in ammonia and hydrogen peroxide. Both α and β phases have undergone dezincification, but the β has been attacked preferentially. The copper redeposited in place of the α phase is more compact than that replacing the β phase, so that the original phase structure is reproduced in the dezincified layer.

PLATE XXXIV 79

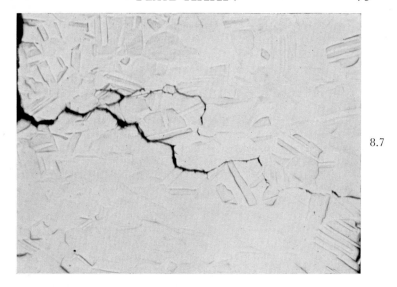

8.7

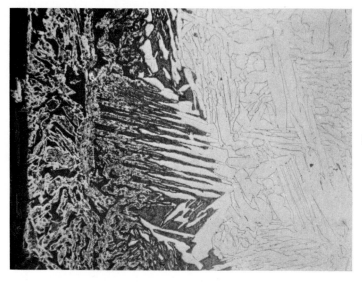

8.8

CHAPTER 9

Tin Bronzes

THE tin bronzes may be classified into two groups.

(1) Alloys containing $< 7\%$ tin, which may be either hot or cold worked and do not usually show the γ phase.

(2) Alloys containing $> 9\%$ tin, which are nearly always used in the cast condition although they can with difficulty be hot worked.

Other alloying elements such as phosphorus, lead, zinc, and nickel are frequently added to improve the properties. Zinc and nickel are readily soluble in the α phase; therefore, with the additions normally made, the microstructures of these ternary alloys are very similar to those of the binary mixture.

Phosphorus is soluble in copper to the extent of $1\cdot2\%$ at $700°$ C— the eutectic temperature. In the presence of tin, the solubility of the phosphorus is decreased and the eutectic structure ($\alpha + Cu_3P$) may occur with phosphorus contents as low as $0\cdot015\%$. Phosphorus may be added to deoxidize bronzes, but the true phosphor bronzes contain $\sim 0\cdot5\%$ phosphorus and are widely used for machine parts which require a bearing surface, e.g. gears and slide-valves.

Small amounts of lead are added to improve machinability and larger amounts (up to 20%) are added to produce bearing alloys. Lead is almost insoluble in tin bronze and is present as isolated globules.

PLATE XXXV

Figures 9.1–9.6

FIG. 9.1. Copper–5%tin, in the as-cast condition. Etched in ferric chloride solution. During casting, dendrites are formed in which there is considerable coring. The centres of the dendrites are copper-rich and appear dark in the micrograph. $\times$ 100.

FIG. 9.2. Copper–10%tin, in the as-cast condition. Etched in potassium dichromate solution. Primary dendrites are formed, but under non-equilibrium conditions some β and subsequently γ phase may be produced. The γ phase eventually undergoes a eutectoid transformation to $(\alpha + \delta)$. The δ is metastable at room temperature. The micrograph shows primary α with the $(\alpha + \delta)$ eutectoid. $\times$ 100.

FIG. 9.3. Copper–10%tin, cast, annealed for 8 h at 650° C, and then cooled rapidly. Etched in ferric chloride solution. During reheating, the δ phase formed on casting dissolves. Very irregular grain shapes of α are produced. $\times$ 100.

FIG. 9.4. Copper–10%tin–0·5%phosphorus, in the as-cast condition. Etched by the polish-attack method using cupric ammonium chloride solution. The binary eutectoid between α and δ appears as light grey and white, whereas in the ternary eutectoid between α, δ, and Cu_3P the latter phase appears dark. $\times$ 1700.

FIG. 9.5. Copper–10%tin–10%lead, in the as-cast condition. Unetched. Globular particles of lead are dispersed throughout the structure. $\times$ 100.

FIG. 9.6. Copper–10% tin–0·5% phosphorus, in the as-cast condition. Etched in potassium dichromate solution. During solidification, the tin- and phosphorus-rich liquid has a melting point considerably lower than that of the first-formed solid. This liquid may be forced between the primary dendrites to the surface of the ingot, so producing a form of inverse segregation known as " tin sweat ". The micrograph shows a section running inwards from the surface of an ingot. To preserve the surface, nickel has been electrodeposited and this appears as a white layer at the bottom of the photograph. The tin- and phosphorus-rich segregate on the surface of the ingot appears dark, as do the solute-rich regions below the surface. The dark areas comprise the binary and ternary eutectoid structures, similar to those shown in Fig. 9.4. $\times$ 150.

PLATE XXXV 83

9.1

9.2

9.3

9.4

9.5

9.6

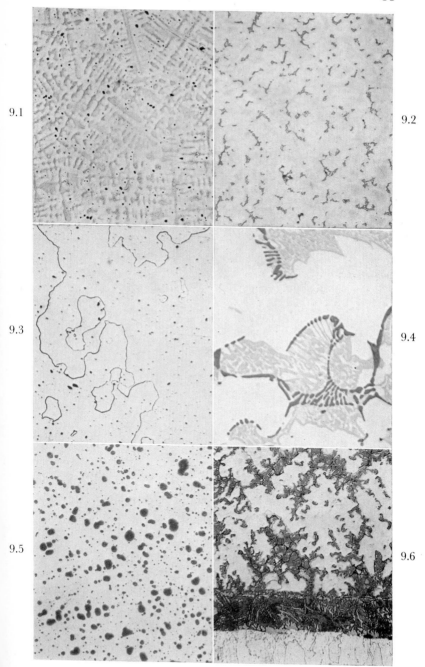

CHAPTER 10

Aluminium Bronzes

ALUMINIUM bronzes are essentially alloys of copper with aluminium in amounts usually ranging from 3 to 12%. The properties of the binary alloys can be modified to advantage by the addition of other alloying elements such as iron, nickel, manganese, and silicon.

The commercial alloys fall into three groups: single-phase α alloys, duplex (α + β) alloys, and complex alloys containing further phases. The α alloys have appreciable ductility and may be cold worked to a considerable degree. They have good corrosion-resistance and are used in the wrought form for chemical plant, salt-water condensers, &c. The duplex and complex alloys have superior casting properties and may also be hot worked by rolling, forging, extruding, and other processes. In addition, their microstructure and properties may be altered considerably by heat-treatment. Their applications include ships' propellers, gears and bearings. They are particularly valuable as bearing materials for use under corrosive conditions, since they combine good wear-resistance with satisfactory corrosion-resistance. They are also finding application for elevated-temperature service, as they have good oxidation-resistance and creep properties.

PLATE XXXVI

Figures 10.1–10.3

FIG. 10.1. Copper–3% aluminium–7% nickel, cold worked and annealed. Etched in 7·5% acidified alcoholic ferric chloride solution. The alloy has recrystallized on annealing to give equiaxed grains containing annealing twins. Dendritic coring is still visible, indicating the persistence of the segregation occurring during solidification. × 100.

FIG. 10.2. Copper–9·8% aluminium–5% iron–5% nickel–0·2% manganese, heated at 1000° C for ½ h and quenched. Etched in 7·5% acidified alcoholic ferric chloride. At 1000° C, the structure should be entirely composed of equiaxed β grains. In this specimen the initial cooling rate from 1000° C was comparatively slow, allowing some light-etching α phase to precipitate at the β grain boundaries and as a Widmanstätten precipitate in their vicinity. The dark-etching β is present, after quenching, in a martensitic form consisting of fine needles difficult to resolve at this magnification. × 40.

FIG. 10.3 Same alloy as in Fig. 10.2, heated to 1000° C, cooled slowly to 975° C, soaked for ½ h, and then quenched. Etched in 7·5% acidified alcoholic ferric chloride. On cooling to 975° C, a small amount of α phase has precipitated as light-etching particles. The α is unchanged on quenching but the dark-etching β is again modified to the martensitic form. × 40.

PLATE XXXVI 85

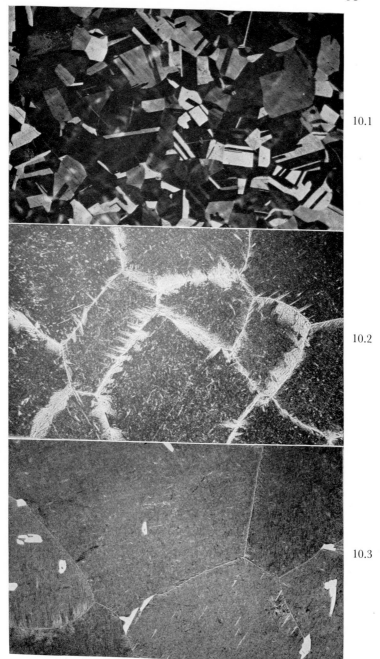

10.1

10.2

10.3

FIG. 10.4. Copper–9·8% aluminium–5% iron–5% nickel–0·2% manganese, heated to 1000° C and then slowly cooled to 950° C, soaked for ½ h, and quenched. Etched in 7·5% acidified alcoholic ferric chloride solution. At 950° C a greater proportion of the light-etching α phase is present in equilibrium with β. The β has again been modified to the martensitic form on quenching. × 40.

FIG. 10.5. Same alloy as Fig. 10.4, heated to 1000° C, slowly cooled to 800° C, soaked for 45 h, and quenched. Etched in 7·5% acidified alcoholic ferric chloride solution. At 800° C both the α and β phases are present initially. On holding at that temperature for a prolonged period the κ phase (based on NiAl) forms and can be seen in the micrograph as rounded greyish particles. × 50.

FIG. 10.6. Same alloy as in Fig. 10.4. Heated to 1000° C, slowly cooled to 700° C, soaked for 70 h, and quenched. At 700° C a smaller proportion of β phase than in Fig. 10.5 was initially present. On soaking for a prolonged period, the β has completely decomposed to κ and α, and precipitation of κ phase has also occurred partially in a Widmanstätten form within the α phase. × 50.

FIG. 10.7. Same alloy as in Fig. 10.4, heated to 1000° C, slowly cooled to 600° C, soaked for 120 h, and quenched. Etched in 7·5% acidified alcoholic ferric chloride solution. The micrograph shows a region which was originally β but which has transformed during holding at 600° C to α and κ. Within the larger globular particles of κ can be seen a Widmanstätten precipitate believed to be α phase. × 500.

PLATE XXXVII 87

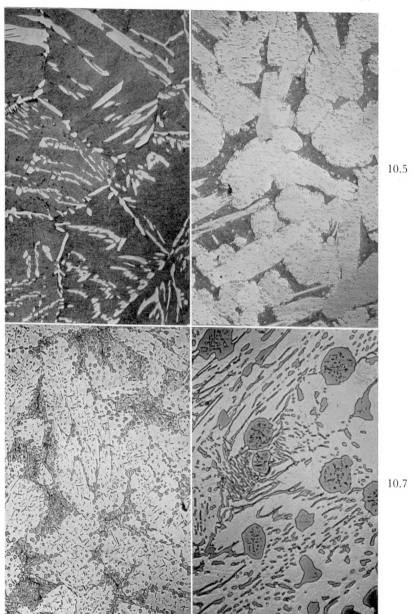

10.5

10.7

CHAPTER 11

Aluminium Alloys

COMMERCIAL aluminium alloys may be divided into two groups, depending upon whether they are to be used in the cast or wrought condition. The casting alloys are usually richer in alloying elements than the wrought alloys, and the microstructures show primary dendrites with a eutectic infilling. The strength of the alloys will depend upon the strength of the primary dendrites and the fineness of the eutectic. Minor alloying additions may be made to modify the eutectic, e.g. the addition of sodium to aluminium–silicon alloys. To strengthen the dendrites and improve the casting properties, alloying additions of zinc, copper, magnesium, iron, and manganese are made, and in such complex alloys many intermetallic phases may be present.

The wrought alloys are relatively low in alloy content and do not, therefore, contain the eutectic in their final condition. Improvement in strength may be obtained by cold working in the case of the aluminium–magnesium alloys, but the more general method is by suitable heat-treatment to give precipitation-hardening. Optical metallography of the wrought alloys in the fully hardened condition will reveal only the grain size and large intermetallics formed from impurities. To study the precipitated phases, the electron microscope must be used. Phase changes in several alloy systems based on aluminium are described in Chapter 7.

PLATE XXXVIII

Figures 11.1–11.3

FIG. 11.1. Aluminium–10% copper, as cast and slowly cooled. Etched in cold 10% ferric nitrate. The structure shows large dendrites of aluminium containing copper in solid solution, surrounded by the eutectic of the solid solution and $CuAl_2$. × 500.

FIG. 11.2. Aluminium–11% silicon, in the chill-cast condition. Etched in 1% hydrofluoric acid. The structure shows primary silicon surrounded by a coarse eutectic of plate-like silicon and the solid solution of silicon in aluminium. × 50.

FIG. 11.3. Aluminium–11% silicon, but now modified by the addition of 0·05% sodium and chill cast. Etched in 1% hydrofluoric acid. The structure shows primary dendrites of aluminium containing silicon in solid solution, surrounded by a fine eutectic of the solid solution and silicon. The effect of the sodium is not only to refine the eutectic but to change the eutectic composition. Thus with 11% silicon the unmodified alloy shows primary silicon, while the modified alloy shows primary dendrites of the aluminium-rich solid solution. × 50.

88

PLATE XXXVIII 89

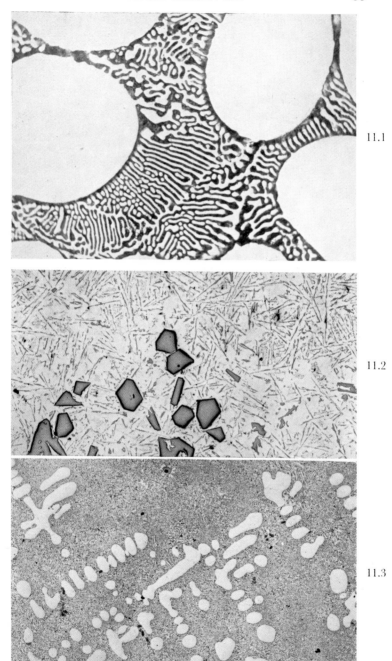

11.1

11.2

11.3

PLATE XXXIX

Figures 11.4–11.6

FIG. 11.4. Aluminium–11% silicon, containing 1% iron and insufficient sodium to produce complete modification. Chill cast, unetched. The primary dendrites are surrounded by a coarse eutectic. Needles of $FeSiAl_3$ are visible and their presence is associated with poor mechanical properties. × 200.

FIG. 11.5. Aluminium–3%copper–5%silicon–0·5%manganese, sand cast. Unetched. The structure shows the " script " form of the compound α-AlFeSi (dark) and $CuAl_2$ (light). × 200.

FIG. 11.6. Aluminium–8% copper–4% manganese, slowly cooled from the liquid state. Etched in 2% nitric acid at 70° C, followed by a dip in cold $12\frac{1}{2}$% sodium hydroxide. The grains of the aluminium-rich solid solution are surrounded by eutectic. Also present are crystals of $MnAl_4$ (grey core) surrounded by $MnAl_6$, which is in turn surrounded by α-CuMn. × 175.

PLATE XXXIX 91

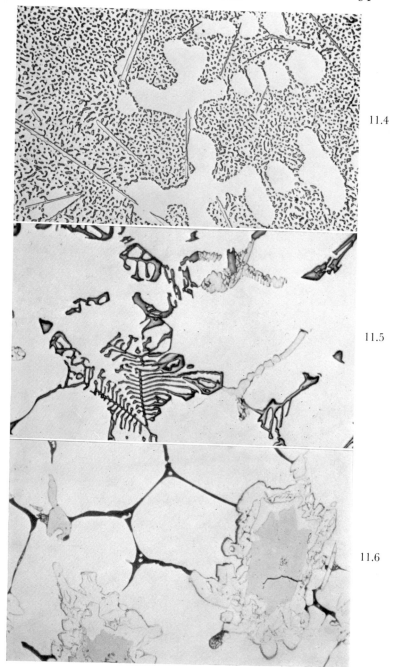

11.4

11.5

11.6

Chapter 12

Magnesium Alloys

MAGNESIUM is seldom used in the pure state, but is alloyed to obtain improvements in strength, toughness, and workability. The chief alloying elements are aluminium, zinc, and manganese, but beryllium, silicon, zirconium, tin, cerium, and other rare earths are often added to produce alloys with special properties. Magnesium alloys are generally used in the cast condition, and in some cases their properties may be improved by heat-treatment. In view of the hexagonal structure of magnesium, the alloys are not easy to work when cold and the wrought alloys have to be deformed while hot. The factors that influence the choice of magnesium alloys are their good casting properties, their high strength : weight ratios, and their good machinability.

PLATE XL

Figures 12.1–12.3

FIG. 12.1. Pure magnesium in the as-cast condition. Etched in 5% nital. A characteristic twin structure is shown. × 150.

FIG. 12.2. Magnesium–8%aluminium–0·5%zinc–0·3%manganese, in the sand-cast condition. Etched in 3% nital. The microstructure shows grains of the δ-phase magnesium-rich solid solution, with a white intergranular γ phase ($Mg_{17}Al_{12}$) and the eutectic of δ and γ. × 50.

FIG. 12.3. Magnesium–4·5% zinc–0·7% zirconium, sand cast and aged for 16 h at 180° C. Etched in 3% nital. The microstructure shows equiaxed grains of the magnesium-rich solid solution, in which there is coring due to the presence of zirconium. Within the grains, precipitates of magnesium–zinc and zirconium–zinc compounds have formed on ageing, but are not resolved. There are also films of MgZn at the grain boundaries. × 600.

PLATE XL 93

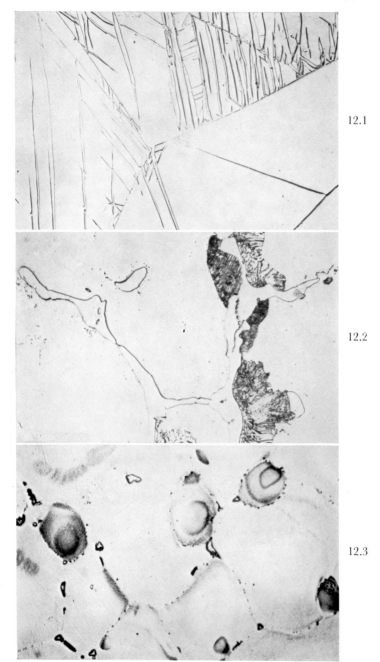

12.1

12.2

12.3

PLATE XLI

Figures 12.4–12.7

FIG. 12.4. Magnesium–2·7% rare earths (cerium 50%, lanthanum 25%, neodymium and praseodymium balance.)–2·5%zinc–0·7%zirconium, sand cast. Etched in 3% nital. Microstructure shows small primary grains of magnesium-rich solid solution and an intergranular precipitate of magnesium–rare earths–zinc compound.   × 150.

FIG. 12.5. Magnesium–2·5% rare earths–2·5% silver–0·7% zirconium, sand cast, solution-treated at 535° C for 8 h. Etched in acetic acid/ glycerol mixture. The microstructure shows equiaxed grains with black compound rich in rare earths at the grain boundaries; this compound was undissolved during solution-treatment. A fine precipitate has formed within the grains but is not clearly resolved.   × 600.

FIG. 12.6. Magnesium–3% thorium–2·25% zinc–0·7% zirconium, sand cast and aged at 315° C for 16 h. Etched in 3% nital. The micro-structure shows equiaxed grains with a magnesium–thorium–zinc compound at the grain boundaries.   × 600.

FIG. 12.7. Magnesium–6% aluminium–1% zinc–0·3% manganese,   cast into a billet and then extruded while hot. Sectioned along the ex-trusion direction and etched in citric acid. During deformation the areas of magnesium–aluminium eutectic have become elongated in the extrusion direction, while the magnesium-rich matrix has partially recrystallized.   × 200.

PLATE XLI   95

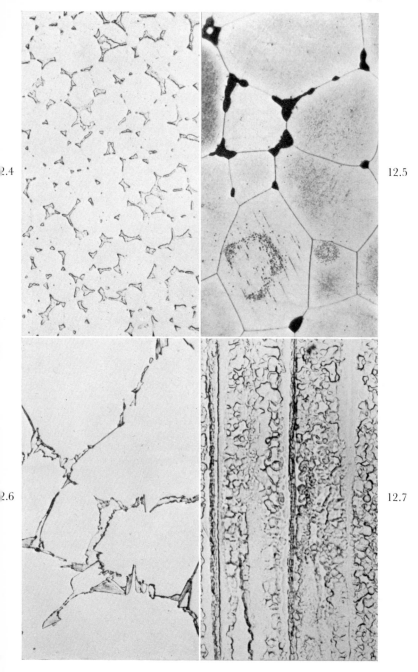

12.4

12.5

12.6

12.7

CHAPTER 13

Titanium Alloys

TITANIUM has a close-packed hexagonal crystal structure (α), which changes to body-centred cubic (β) when heated above 880° C. Alloying elements may raise or depress the temperature of this allotropic change. With suitable alloying additions, the β phase may be retained on quenching from above the transformation temperature. With a smaller alloy content, the β phase may decompose by a shear transformation to α on quenching. On slow cooling or ageing the metastable β, the α phase may be precipitated in a Widmanstätten form. Hydrogen is soluble in α-titanium at high temperatures, and precipitates as the hydride on cooling.

PLATE XLII

Figures 13.1–13.4

FIG. 13.1. Titanium–5·2% manganese, heated at 950° C and water-quenched. Etched in $1\frac{1}{2}\%$ hydrofluoric acid with 3% nitric acid in aqueous solution. Equiaxed grains of retained β. × 100.

FIG. 13.2. Titanium–3·5% manganese, heated at 950° C and water-quenched. Etched in $1\frac{1}{2}\%$ hydrofluoric acid with 3% nitric acid in aqueous solution, and stained in $\frac{1}{2}\%$ hydrofluoric acid in hot water. Needles of martensitic α in a β matrix. The lower manganese content, as compared with the alloy shown in Fig. 13.1, is insufficient to retain the β phase completely and some of it has undergone a shear transformation. × 300.

FIG. 13.3. Titanium–4% aluminium–4% manganese, hot rolled at 900° C, reheated to 900° C, and water-quenched. Etched in 18 g benzalkonium chloride + 35 ml alcohol + 40 ml glycerol + 5% hydrofluoric acid. Equiaxed particles of α phase in a martensitic α matrix. The equiaxed grains form before quenching, when the alloy is in a two-phase field. × 500.

FIG. 13.4. Titanium–10% aluminium, air-cooled from 1200° C. Etched in $1\frac{1}{2}\%$ hydrofluoric acid with 3% nitric acid in aqueous solution. Widmanstätten precipitate of α formed by nucleation and growth in the β during cooling. × 100.

PLATE XLII 97

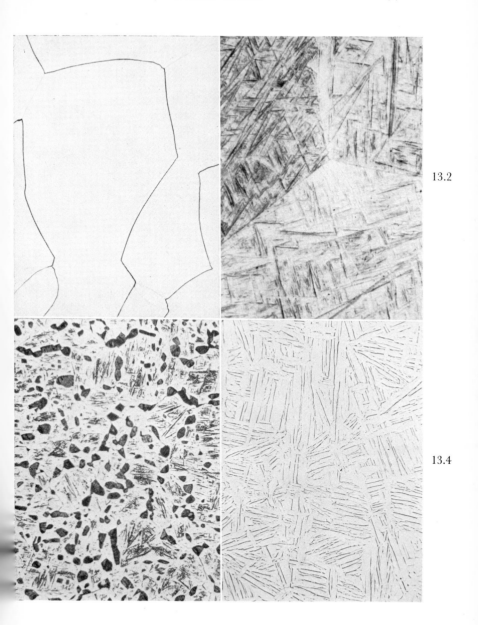

13.2

13.4

PLATE XLIII

Figures 13.5 and 13.6

FIG. 13.5. Iodide titanium–7% chromium, heated to 1000° C, air-cooled, heated at 693° C for 1 week, and water-quenched. Etched in 40% hydrofluoric acid in glycerol. Widmanstätten precipitate of α in a β matrix. The chromium stabilizes the β phase sufficiently to prevent its decomposition during air-cooling but subsequent prolonged ageing causes a partial transformation to α.   × 250.

FIG. 13.6. Iodide titanium–0·01% oxygen–0·01% nitrogen, exposed to hydrogen at 500° C and then cooled slowly to room temperature. Electropolished and etched in 2% hydrofluoric acid with 5% nitric acid in water. Equiaxed grains of α-titanium containing fine needles of TiH which have been precipitated on cooling.   × 100.

PLATE XLIII   99

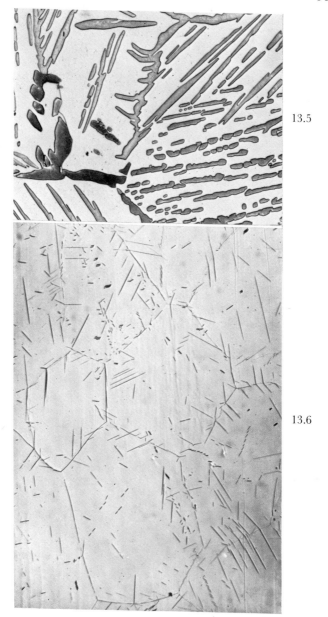

13.5

13.6

CHAPTER 14

Bearing Alloys

BEARINGS usually run with a thin oil film separating them from the rotating shaft. If this film could be preserved, then no wear would take place on the metallic surfaces, but this condition is difficult to maintain. To minimize the risk of seizure when breakdown of the oil film occurs, alloys having low coefficients of friction have been developed. These are usually of the two-phase type, one phase being considerably softer then the other, while the melting point of the soft phase should be lower than that of the hard phase. There are two main types of bearing alloys. In the first case, the softer phase forms the matrix within which the particles of the hard phase are distributed. In the other case, the continuous phase is the hard material with the soft phase distributed within it, but good bearing properties are also obtained if the soft phase is plated on to the hard phase.

In service, the soft phase melts as a result of frictional heating and flows over the surface of the hard phase giving a layer of $\sim 10^{-4}$ to 10^{-5} cm thickness. As the soft layer wears away, it may be replenished by further exudation, and in this respect the dispersed-phase bearings are better than the layer bearings. However, with the layer bearings a variety of hard and soft layers may be produced which it would be difficult to obtain as dispersed phases. The role of the hard phase is merely to strengthen the alloy, so that greater loads can be carried than if a homogeneous soft-phase alloy were used. A further advantage of a two-phase structure is that, because of exudation of the soft phase, crevices may be produced which will act as small reservoirs for lubricant.

Thermal cycling occurs in a bearing as a result of starting and stopping. If the bearing alloy contains a thermally anisotropic phase, then the thermally induced stresses may lead to fatigue failure. Failure of tin-based bearing alloys often takes place by thermal fatigue (see Chapter 4, p. 40).

Soft-Matrix Alloys

Alloys in this group are tin- or lead-based; the alloying elements added are antimony and copper, which give dispersions of hard intermetallic compounds within the soft matrix when the alloy is cast. The tin-based alloys will run at higher bearing loads but are more expensive than the lead-based ones. Since tin-based alloys have an anisotropic matrix, they are more prone to thermal fatigue than are the lead-based alloys.

100

Hard-Matrix Alloys

Copper-based alloys having lead as a dispersed phase make very successful bearing materials. Layered bearings may be produced with a steel base and a wide variety of soft layers. Self-lubricating bearings can be obtained by impregnating porous compacts with oil or by making graphite/metal mixtures using powder-metallurgical techniques.

H

The Microstructure of Metals

PLATE XLIV

Figures 14.1 and 14.2

FIG. 14.1. Tin–10% antimony–8% copper (tin-based white metal). Etched in 10% ferric chloride. During cooling from the liquid phase, CuSn precipitates as needles, forming star-shaped dendrites; at a lower temperature SnSb precipitates as cubes, which become enmeshed in the CuSn dendrites. The matrix is tin containing a small amount of antimony and copper in solid solution. × 35.

FIG. 14.2. Lead–13% antimony–12% tin–0·5% copper (lead-based white metal). Etched in 10% ferric chloride. Small cubes of SbSn are formed in a matrix consisting of lead-rich dendrites, with an infilling of the lead–tin eutectic. × 500.

PLATE XLIV   103

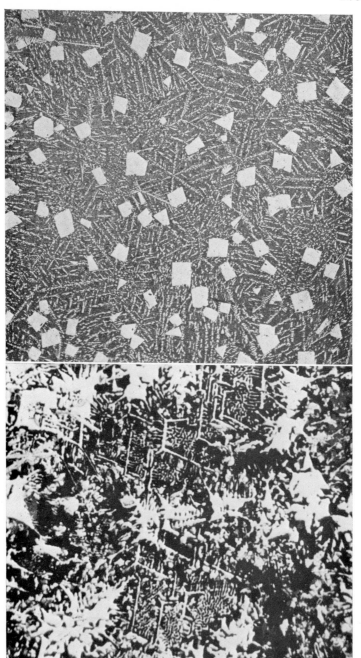

14.1

14.2

PLATE XLV

Figures 14.3–14.6

Fig. 14.3. Tin–7% antimony–3% copper, bonded to a nodular ferritic cast iron. Etched in 2% nital. The light-etching CuSn and SnSb are dispersed in a tin-rich matrix. The cast-iron base shows graphite nodules. × 150.

Fig. 14.4. Copper–30% lead, prepared by compacting a powder of copper and lead. Unetched. The continuous white phase is copper, with lead at the grain boundaries. × 100.

Fig. 14.5. Copper–30% lead, with an overlay of lead–10% tin. The narrow overlay on the left-hand side links with the lead in the copper matrix. × 220.

Fig. 14.6. Aluminium–20% tin–10% copper, bonded to steel. Unetched. The aluminium-rich matrix has a tin-rich phase at the grain boundaries. The bonding layer, on the right-hand side next to the steel, is low in tin. × 100.

PLATE XLV 105

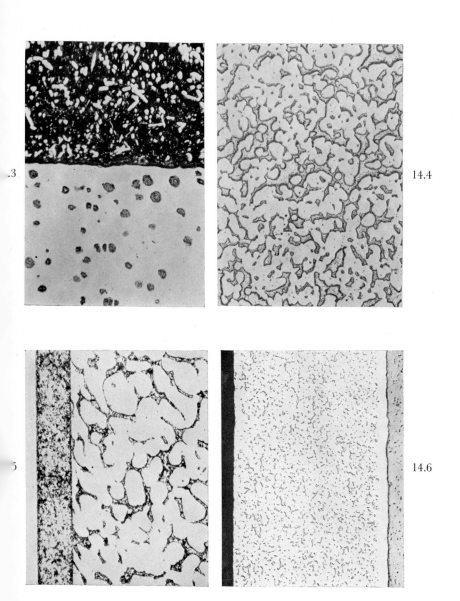

14.3

14.4

14.5

14.6

PLATE XLVI

Figures 14.7–14.9

FIG. 14.7. Copper–10% tin–6% carbon. The material has been made by pressing and sintering a bronze powder and finely divided graphite. Unetched. A uniform distribution of the graphite has been obtained, which gives a very good self-lubricating bearing. × 100.

FIG. 14.8. Similar specimen to that shown in Fig. 14.7 but a shadowed plastic replica has been prepared. The graphite forms as films around the grain boundaries, as well as being present as more massive particles. Electron micrograph. × 7500.

FIG. 14.9. Tin–5% antimony–0·5% copper, thermally cycled 50 times between 30 and 150° C. Unetched. Because of the anisotropy of thermal expansion of the tin-rich matrix, fatigue-type cracks develop on thermal cycling. × 100.

PLATE XLVI 107

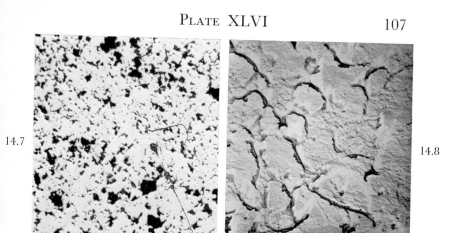

14.7

14.8

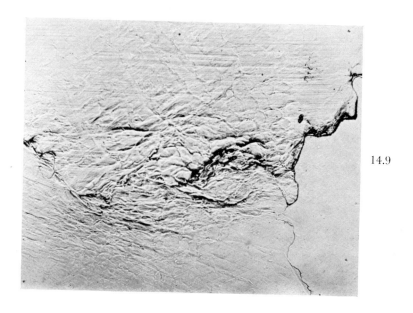

14.9

Chapter 15

Special-Purpose Alloys

(1) *Diecasting Alloys* are usually of low melting point and are capable of forming a good impression of a mould. The alloys may be poured into the mould, so forming a gravity diecasting, or forced into the mould to give a pressure diecasting. Permanent metal moulds are used and this enables castings of high dimensional accuracy to be obtained. The most commonly used diecasting alloys have a zinc base, but other alloys which may be used are aluminium-, magnesium-, tin-, lead-, or copper-based. (Plate XLVII.)

(2) *Hard Metals* are required for cutting tools, wire-drawing dies, and components subjected to heavy wear or abrasion. The alloys are produced by cold pressing powdered carbides of tungsten, titanium, or tantalum, mixed with powdered cobalt or nickel. The compact is subsequently sintered at a high temperature to give a carbide aggregate bonded with a metallic element. (Plate XLVIII.)

(3) *High-Temperature Alloys* have been developed to have good creep properties at high temperatures. The most widely used alloys are those based on a nickel/chromium mixture (e.g. Nimonic alloys). Various other elements such as aluminium, titanium, iron, and cobalt are added to produce precipitating phases which confer good creep-resistance on the alloy. Good creep properties may also be obtained by producing a dispersed oxide in a metallic matrix by powder-metallurgical techniques. (Plates XLIX and L.)

(4) *Ferromagnetic Alloys* are of two main types: (i) the magnetically soft, which are usually mechanically soft and are of annealed single-phase composition, and (ii) the magnetically hard, which are usually mechanically hard and consist of cold-worked single-phase alloys or two-phase alloys having a finely dispersed ferromagnetic phase in a paramagnetic matrix. In the single-phase alloy, superimposed upon the normal metallurgical structure, there are domains in which each of the constituent atoms has its magnetic orientation in the same direction. Under the action of an externally applied magnetic field, the domains may be aligned and the material becomes ferromagnetic. With an ideally soft material, on removing the external magnetic field, there is no permanently retained ferromagnetism, i.e. the domains once more become randomly oriented.

With a magnetically hard alloy, the domains retain their alignment on the removal of a magnetic field. In cold-worked materials, the internal strains prevent realignment of the domains, and in the two-phase alloys each dispersed-phase particle forms a single domain which, once aligned, is difficult to realign. (Plate LI.)

PLATE XLVII

Figures 15.1 and 15.2

FIG. 15.1. Zinc-base diecasting alloy (containing 4% aluminium, 0·05% magnesium), in the sand-cast condition. Etched in 2·5% nital. On cooling, zinc-rich dendrites form followed by a eutectic of two zinc-rich phases containing 83% zinc (α') and 99% zinc (β). The α' phase subsequently decomposes at 275° C, via a eutectoid reaction, to give an aluminium-rich α phase and the β phase.   × 500.

FIG. 15.2. Same as a Fig. 15.1 but in the chill-cast condition.   With a more rapid cooling rate, smaller dendrites are produced, while the eutectic structure is not resolved.   × 300.

PLATE XLVII 111

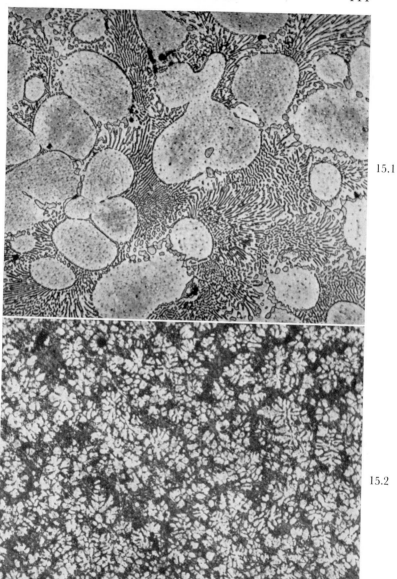

15.1

15.2

PLATE XLVIII

Figures 15.3–15.5

FIG. 15.3. Hard metal (containing 89% tungsten carbide, 11% cobalt). Polished with diamond powder and etched in alkaline potassium ferricyanide. Angular particles of WC are bonded by light-etching cobalt. × 1500.

FIG. 15.4. Hard metal (containing 77% tungsten carbide, 7% titanium carbide, 6% cobalt). Polished with diamond powder and etched in alkaline potassium ferricyanide. × 1500.

FIG. 15.5. Hard metal (containing 80% tungsten carbide, 8% cobalt, 12% titanium carbide + tantalum carbide). This gives a multicarbide dispersion with cobalt bonding. The carbides can be distinguished chiefly by colour difference: WC pale grey, TiC pale pinkish brown, TaC dark pinkish brown. In the micrograph the massive triangular particles are WC, the massive irregular particles are solid solutions of mixed carbides, the small dark particles are TaC, while the light areas are the cobalt bonding. × 1500.

PLATE XLVIII   113

15.3

15.4

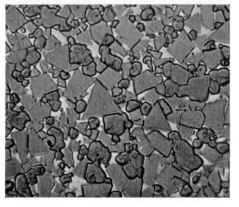

15.5

The Microstructure of Metals

PLATE XLIX

Figures 15.6 and 15.7

FIG. 15.6. Nimonic 80A (Cr 20, Co 0·8, Ti 2·6, Al 1·2, C 0·05%, balance nickel), heated at 1080° C for 10 min, then reheated to 925° C for 1 h and 750° C for 4 h. Etched electrolytically in 10% phosphoric acid in water. A carbon film was deposited, and then stripped by re-etching in the same solution. The extraction replica removed the γ' particles which are present as small cubes within the grains, but the carbide particles at the grain boundaries were not removed. Electron micrograph. × 3000.

FIG. 15.7. Same specimen as Fig. 15.6 but etched electrolytically in a solution of 100 ml hydrochloric acid, 500 ml nitric acid, 25 g cupric chloride, 25 g ferric chloride, 1200 ml water. A carbon film was deposited and then stripped by re-etching in the same solution. The extraction replica removed the carbides ($M_{23}C_6$) which were present at the grain and twin boundaries. The γ' phase was not removed. Electron micrograph. × 3000.

PLATE XLIX 115

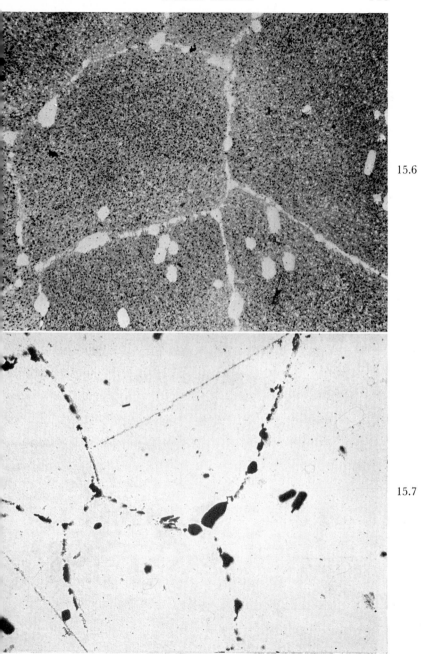

15.6

15.7

PLATE L

Figures 15.8–15.10

FIG. 15.8. Nimonic 90 (Cr 20, Co 15, Fe 5, Si 1·5, Ti 2, Al 1·5, Mo 1·0, C 0·1%, balance nickel), heated at 1080° C for 1 h, then reheated to 700° C for 16 h. Etched in 10% phosphoric acid. A carbon film was deposited and stripped by electropolishing in a mixture of 10% perchloric acid in acetic acid. Small particles of the γ′ phase, precipitated at 700° C, have been extracted on to the replica. Electron micrograph.   × 85,000.

FIG. 15.9. Nimonic 105 (Cr 15·5, Co 20, Ti 1·3, Al 4·5, Mo 5·0, C 0·07%, balance nickel), heated to 1150° C for 1½ h, then to 1080° C for 8 h, and finally to 800° C for 16 h. Carbon-extraction replica prepared as in Fig. 15.8. The γ′ particles are larger and the volume fraction of the precipitates is greater than in Fig. 15.8. Electron micrograph. × 85,000.

FIG. 15.10. Nimonic 115 (Cr 15, Co 15, Ti 4·0, Al 5·0, Mo 3·5, C 0·1%, balance nickel), heated to 1180° C for 2 h, then to 1050° C for 1 h. Carbon-extraction replica prepared as in Fig. 15.8. The well-developed cubes of γ′ phase form with their faces parallel to the {100} planes of the γ. Between the larger cubes, smaller cubes have precipitated. The alloys shown in Figs. 15.8–15.10 have shown a progressive improvement in creep properties, and the series illustrate some of the microstructural reasons for this improvement, namely, changes in the precipitate dispersion and an increase in the volume fraction of the dispersed phase. Electron micrograph.   × 17,000.

PLATE L   117

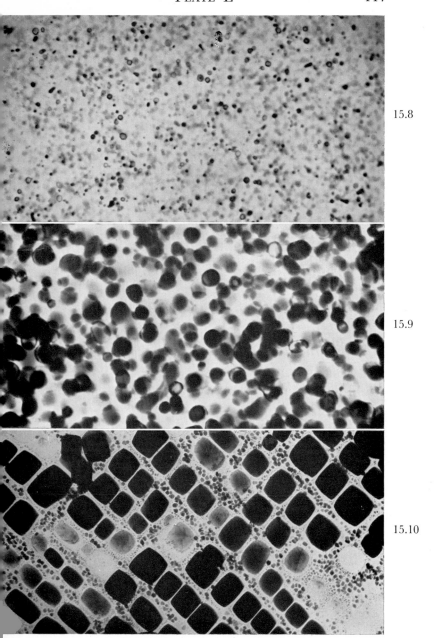

15.8

15.9

15.10

I

PLATE LI

Figures 15.11–15.13

Fig. 15.11. S.A.P. 930 (7% Al_2O_3, balance aluminium). Thin foil prepared by electropolishing and examined by transmission in the electron microscope. The matrix consists of very fine grains of aluminium, 0·3–0·8 μm in dia.; particles of oxide are present at the grain boundaries and within the grains. Electron micrograph. × 25,000.

Fig. 15.12. Alcomax III (Co 24, Ni 13·5, Al 8, Cu 3, Nb 0·5%, balance iron), heated to 1250° C and cooled at 1·2 degC/sec in a field of 1000 Oe, then tempered at 590° C for 48 h. Thin foil prepared by electropolishing and examined by transmission in the electron microscope: (*a*) parallel to magnetic field; (*b*) perpendicular to magnetic field. The ferromagnetic precipitates are rod-like and form with their long axes parallel to the magnetic field. Electron micrographs. × 120,000.

Fig. 15.13. Permalloy (iron–20% nickel), evaporated to form a thin foil ∼300 Å thick and then examined by transmission in the electron microscope using slightly out-of-focus conditions. The grain size is ∼500 Å. One magnetic domain exists throughout the thickness of the film. As the electron beam passes through the film it is bent, as shown in Fig. 15.A. This gives alternate convergence and divergence

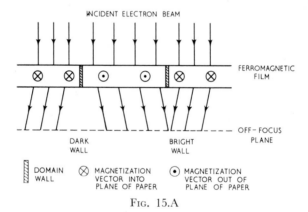

Fig. 15.A

of the beams in the regions of the domain walls, which will therefore appear alternately light and dark when the off-focus plane is imaged. In this case the domain size is considerably larger than the grain size. The cross-band structure of alternate contrast on each domain wall, and the spot of the same contrast as the wall between the cross-bands, are a result of effects associated with the magnetic properties of thin foils. Electron micrograph. × 6000.

PLATE LI   119

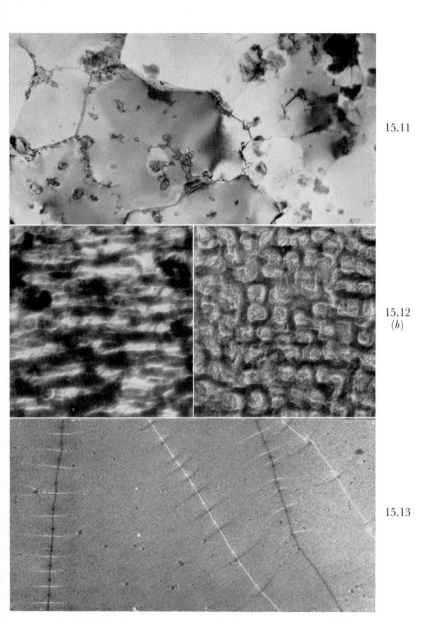

15.11

15.12
(b)

15.13

SECTION III. FERROUS ALLOYS

CHAPTER 16

The Effect of Carbon Content on the Structure of Normalized Iron–Carbon Alloys

AT room temperature, iron has a body-centred cubic structure (α), but on heating to 910° C it undergoes an allotropic transformation to give a face-centred cubic form (γ). Carbon is only slightly soluble in α-iron but may dissolve to the extent of 1·7% in the γ form. The solid solution of carbon in α is known as ferrite, and that in γ is known as austenite. The allotropic transformation temperature is decreased by the addition of carbon and reaches a minimum of 723° C, corresponding to the addition of 0·8% carbon (the eutectoid point). The alloys of iron with <0·05% carbon are usually known as irons. At higher carbon contents, up to 1·7%, the materials are known as steels; hypo-eutectoid steels contain <0·8% carbon, hypereutectoid steels are in the range 0·8–1·7% carbon.

PLATE LII

Figures 16.1 and 16.2

FIG. 16.1. Wrought iron in the as-forged condition. Etched in 2% nital. The structure shows equiaxed ferrite grains with small particles of slag at the boundaries. The larger slag inclusions show a two-phase structure with dendrites of FeO in a matrix of $2FeO.SiO_2$. × 200.

FIG. 16.2. Armco iron in the normalized condition. Etched in 2% nital. The structure shows equiaxed grains of ferrite. The darker particles are chiefly oxides, but there are some sulphide inclusions. × 200.

PLATE LII 121

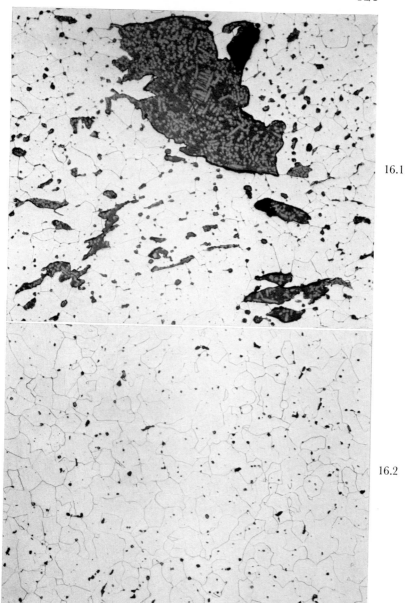

16.1

16.2

PLATE LIII

Figures 16.3–16.6

FIG. 16.3. 0·1% Carbon steel in the normalized condition. Etched in 2% nital. The structure shows polygonal ferrite grains and small regions of the ferrite–iron carbide eutectoid pearlite. The eutectoid is not resolved at this magnification. × 200.

FIG. 16.4. 0·35% Carbon steel in the normalized condition. Etched in 2% nital. With increasing carbon content the proportion of eutectoid increases. × 300.

FIG. 16.5. 0·55% Carbon steel in the normalized condition. Etched in 2% nital. During transformation from the austenitic region, ferrite is nucleated preferentially at the austenite boundaries. The remaining austenite rapidly reaches eutectoid composition, when it transforms to give pearlite. Thus the pro-eutectoid ferrite outlines the prior austenite grains. × 600.

FIG. 16.6. 0·80% Carbon steel in the normalized condition. Etched in 2% nital. The structure is entirely pearlitic. Each prior austenite grain has transformed to give several pearlite colonies which can be distinguished by their slight differences in response to etching. × 200.

PLATE LIII   123

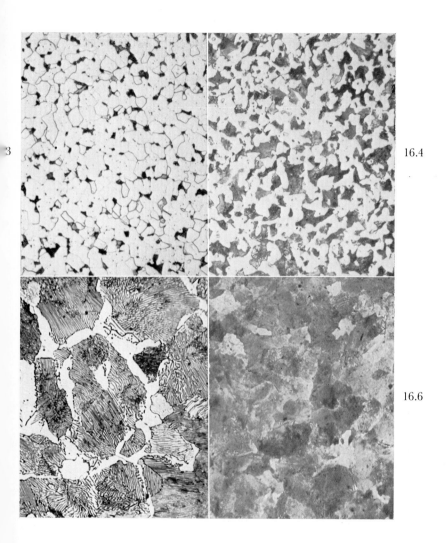

PLATE LIV

Plates 16.7–16.9

FIG. 16.7. 0·8% Carbon steel, examined at high magnification. Etched in 2% nital. The individual plates of cementite are clearly resolved and the different pearlite colonies can be observed. The cementite lamellæ are probably equally spaced, and the apparent differences arise from the plane of section cutting the plates at different angles. × 1500.

FIG. 16.8. 1·2% Carbon steel in the normalized condition. Etched in boiling alkaline sodium picrate for 5 min. Pro-eutectoid cementite forms at the prior austenite grain boundaries and during etching it is stained black. Some graphitization of the cementite has occurred to give the large inclusions of graphite, chiefly at the austenite boundaries. × 150.

FIG. 16.9. 1·4% Carbon steel in the normalized condition. Etched in 2% nital. Pro-eutectoid cementite has formed around the austenite grains and as a Widmanstätten precipitate within the grains. The remaining austenite has transformed to fine pearlite. Electron micrograph of plastic replica. × 3000.

PLATE LIV   125

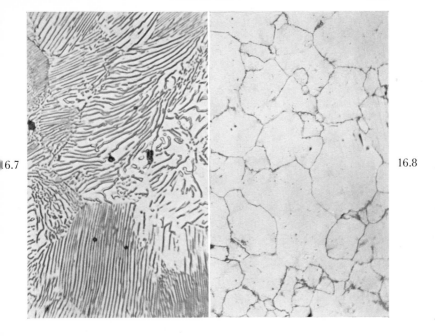

16.7

16.8

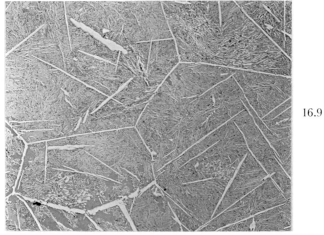

16.9

CHAPTER 17

Influence of Rapid Cooling Rates on the Structure
of Steels

WHEN steel is cooled rapidly from the austenitic region, phase changes involving nucleation and diffusion-controlled growth may be suppressed. In this case the austenite transforms at a lower temperature by a diffusionless shear transformation to give martensite having a body-centred tetragonal structure. The microstructure of the martensite depends upon the temperature at which it forms from the austenite, which in turn depends upon the carbon content. Thus, low-carbon martensites have a different appearance from those of high carbon content. If the cooling is not sufficiently rapid to suppress entirely the diffusion-controlled transformation, some decomposition of austenite to give a fine aggregate of cementite and ferrite may occur at the austenite grain boundaries.

In high-carbon and alloy steels, some austenite may be retained after quenching to room temperature.

PLATE LV

Figures 17.1 and 17.2

FIG. 17.1. 0·34% Carbon steel, heated to 900° C and water-quenched. Etched in 2% nital. The acicular structure is not clearly marked and the structure is not so obviously martensitic as that found with higher carbon contents (cf. Fig. 17.3). The austenite grain boundaries are outlined by a high-temperature transformation product. × 400.

FIG. 17.2. 0·55% Carbon steel, heated to 850° C and water-quenched. Etched in 2% nital. The austenite grain boundaries are outlined by a high-temperature transformation product. × 750.

PLATE LV   127

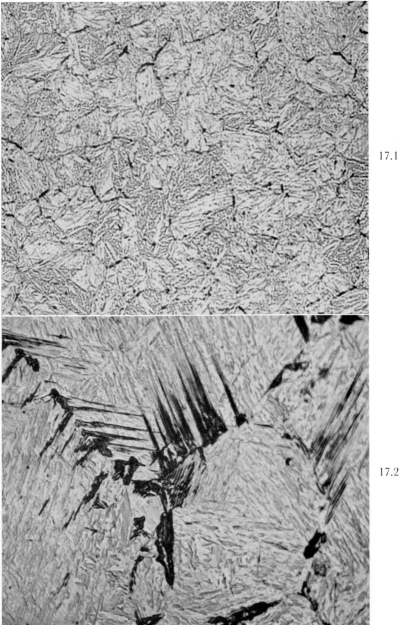

17.1

17.2

Plate LVI

Figures 17.3 and 17.4

Fig. 17.3. 1·2% Carbon steel, heated to 960° C and water-quenched. Etched in 2% nital. The more sharply defined structure is characteristic of high-carbon martensite. Between the acicular markings there are regions of untransformed austenite and the austenite grain boundaries are clearly visible. × 750.

Fig. 17.4. 0·14% Carbon steel, heated to 920° C and water-quenched. Electrolytically machined to give a thin foil 100 μm thick and then electro-thinned to 2000 Å. Examined by transmission in the electron microscope. With a low carbon content, the M_s temperature is ~500° C and the structure produced is that of bunches of needles having their long axes parallel to the $\langle 111 \rangle$ direction of the body-centred structure, which was originally a $\langle 110 \rangle$ direction in the parent austenite. Within the needles there is a high dislocation density. Electron micrograph. × 80,000.

PLATE LVI 129

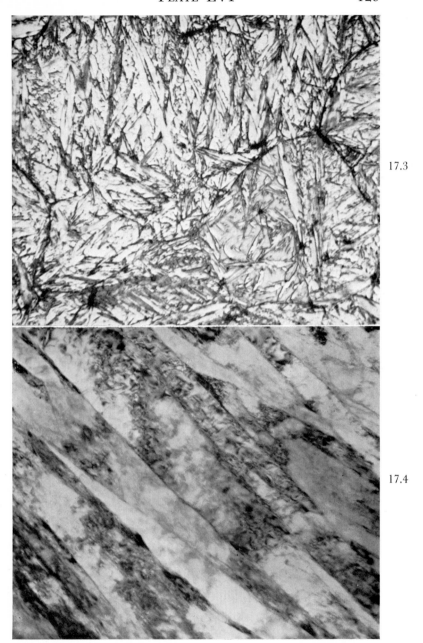

17.3

17.4

PLATE LVII

Figures 17.5 and 17.6

FIG. 17.5. 1·0% Carbon steel, heated to 800° C and water-quenched. Electrolytically machined to give a foil 100 μm thick and then electro-thinned to 2000 Å. Examined by transmission in the electron micro-scope. With a high carbon content, the M_s temperature is ∼200° C and the structure produced is that of plates. The habit plane of the martensite is $(225)_\gamma$. Within the martensite plates, there are fine twins on the $\{112\}$ martensite planes, with widths varying from 50 to 200 Å. No dislocations can be observed within the twins. Electron micrograph. × 80,000.

FIG. 17.6. Iron–20% nickel–0·8% carbon alloy steel heated to 1000° C and then quenched to −95° C. Electrolytically machined to give a foil 100 μm thick and then electro-thinned to 2000 Å. Examined by transmission in the electron microscope. With the heat-treatment given, some austenite has been retained; this can be seen adjacent to a twinned martensite plate. Within the retained austenite there is a high dislocation density. The dislocations are produced by the stresses generated during the shear transformation. Electron micrograph. × 20,000.

Plate LVII   131

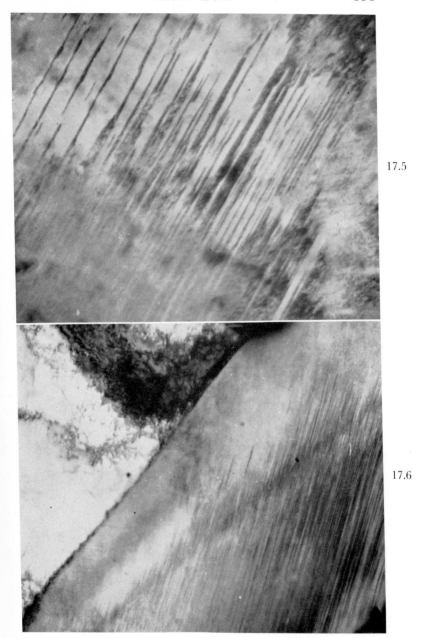

17.5

17.6

CHAPTER 18

Isothermal Transformations

THE temperature-dependence of the mode of austenite decomposition can be studied by rapidly cooling a steel from the austenitic region to the required temperature, maintaining specimens at that temperature for predetermined periods, and then quenching to room temperature. With eutectoid steel, the isothermal decomposition product at temperatures between 700 and 500° C is pearlite. The interlamellar spacing of the pearlite decreases as the temperature of transformation is lowered until, at 500° C, a new mode of decomposition occurs giving rise to upper bainite. Another mode of decomposition occurs as the transformation temperature is reduced further, so giving lower bainite. The two forms of bainite are very similar to the structures developed on tempering the needle and plate forms of martensite described in Chapter 17.

In hypo-eutectoid steels, the form of the pro-eutectoid ferrite changes as the transformation temperature is decreased. In some steels with a low alloy content, a bainitic form of ferrite can be produced by continuous cooling from the austenitic region.

PLATE LVIII

Figures 18.1–18.3

This series illustrates 0·8% carbon steel, heated to 850° C, quenched to 675° C, and maintained at that temperature for different periods. The austenite has decomposed partially to give pearlite and then, on quenching to room temperature, the previously untransformed austenite has been converted into martensite. Etched in 2% nital.

FIG. 18.1. Isothermally transformed for 1 min to give 1% transformation.

FIG. 18.2. Isothermally transformed for 5 min to give 25% transformation.

FIG. 18.3. Isothermally transformed for 8 min to give 50% transformation.
× 750.

PLATE LVIII 133

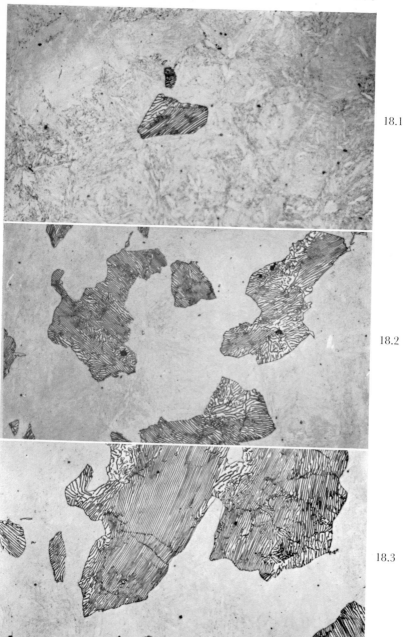

18.1

18.2

18.3

K

PLATE LIX

Figures 18.4–18.6

FIG. 18.4. 0·8% Carbon steel, heated at 850° C, quenched to 500° C, and maintained at temperature for 5 min. Etched in 2% picral. A plastic replica was prepared and shadowed at an angle of 27° with chromium. The austenite has transformed partially to give a fine pearlite, and then an upper bainite. The carbide spacing in the upper bainite is larger than the carbide spacing in the fine pearlite. Electron micrograph. × 10,000.

FIG. 18.5. 0·8% Carbon steel, heated to 850° C, quenched, and isothermally transformed for 20 sec at 450° C. Etched in 2% picral. 50% of the austenite has transformed to give upper bainite. The bainitic areas extend by the growth of needles parallel to their long axis. × 1500.

FIG. 18.6. Same specimen as Fig. 18.5 but transformed for 2 min at 450° C to give 100% transformation to upper bainite. × 1500.

PLATE LIX 135

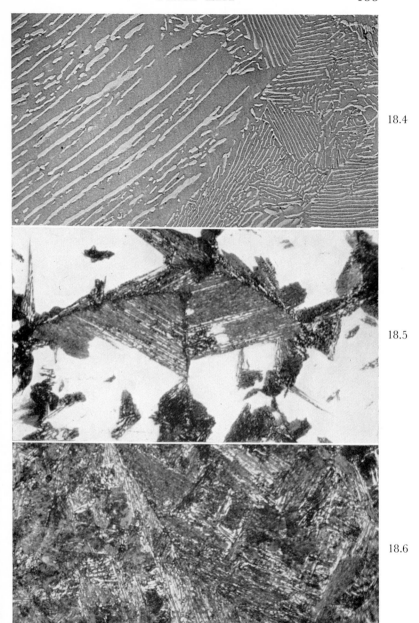

18.4

18.5

18.6

PLATE LX

Figures 18.7–18.9

FIG. 18.7. 0·8% Carbon steel, heated to 850° C, quenched, and isothermally transformed for 20 sec at 450° C. Etched in 2% picral. A plastic replica was prepared and shadowed at an angle of 27° with chromium. 50% of the austenite has transformed to upper bainite. The needle-like growth of the bainite into the austenite is shown, together with the carbides which have formed parallel to the long axis of the needles. Electron micrograph. × 8000.

FIG. 18.8. 0·8% Carbon steel, heated to 850° C, quenched to 450° C, and maintained at temperature for 2 min. Etched in 2% picral. A plastic replica was prepared and shadowed at an angle of 27° with chromium. 100% of the austenite has transformed to upper bainite. The long laths of carbide are formed along the needle axes. Electron micrograph. × 8000.

FIG. 18.9. 1·0% Carbon, 1·0% chromium, 0·5% molybdenum steel, heated to 1050° C, then quenched to 350° C and maintained at temperature for 1¾ h to give upper bainite. Thin foil prepared by jet-machining and electropolishing and then examined by transmission in the electron microscope. Between the carbide platelets there is a high dislocation density in the ferrite. Electron micrograph. × 30,000.

PLATE LX   137

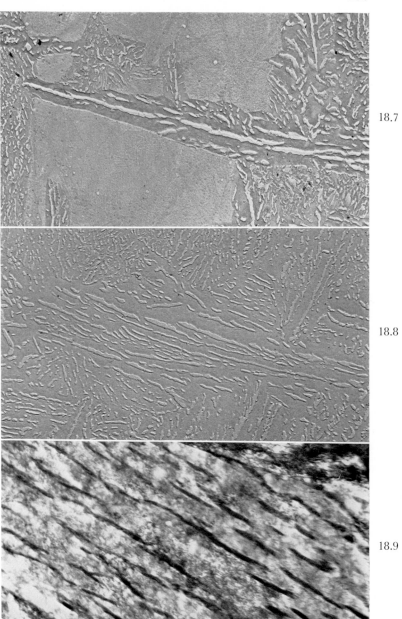

18.7

18.8

18.9

PLATE LXI

Figures 18.10–18.13

FIG. 18.10. 0·1% Carbon, ½% molybdenum, 0·003% boron steel, heated to 950° C and air-cooled. Etched in 2% nital. During cooling the pro-eutectoid ferrite has formed by an upper-bainitic type of transformation. × 750.

FIG. 18.11. Same specimen as Fig. 18.10 but a Formvar replica has been prepared after etching in 2% nital. An upper bainitic substructure is visible within the ferrite grains. The carbon-enriched austenite has transformed to give a structure characteristic of an upper bainite in a eutectoid steel. Electron micrograph. × 3000.

FIGS 18.12 and 18.13. 0·8% Carbon steel, heated to 850° C, then quenched to 260° C and maintained at temperature for 5 and 30 min to give 1 and 25% transformation to lower bainite. Etched in 2% picral. The structure is very similar to that of martensite, but the bainite is more readily etched than the martensite. × 1000.

PLATE LXI   139

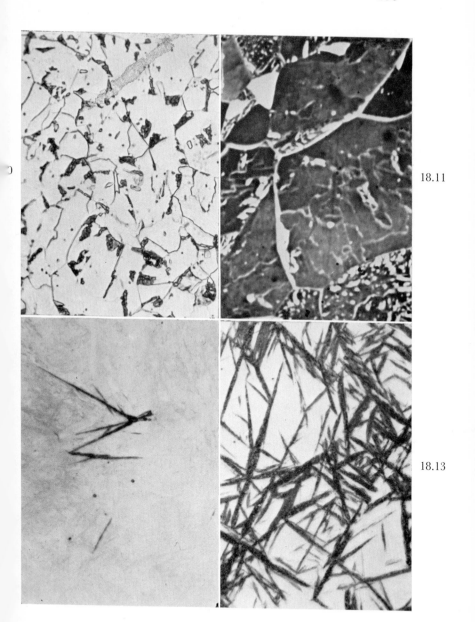

18.11

18.13

PLATE LXII

Figures 18.14 and 18.5

FIG. 18.14. 0·8% Carbon steel, heated to 850° C, quenched to 260° C and maintained at temperature for 2½ h. Etched in 2% picral. A plastic replica was prepared and shadowed at an angle of 45° with chromium. 100% of the austenite has transformed to lower bainite. The laths of lower bainite contain smaller laths of carbide which have formed at an angle of 55° to the long axes of the laths (cf. Fig. 18.8.) Electron micrograph. × 8000.

FIG. 18.15. 0·65%Carbon, 1%molybdenum steel, heated to 1100° C, quenched to 275° C and maintained at temperature for 11 min to give lower bainite. A thin foil was prepared by jet-machining and electropolishing, then examined by transmission in the electron microscope. Small carbides have precipitated on planes parallel to the twins which have formed as in martensite. Some fine twins are present in the structure (cf. Fig. 18.9). Electron micrograph. × 30,000.

PLATE LXII 141

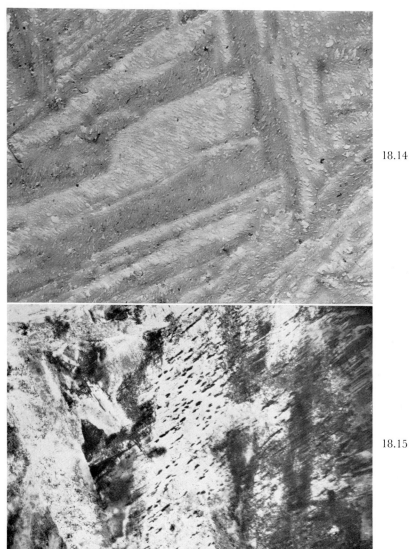

18.14

18.15

CHAPTER 19

Tempering of Plain Carbon Steels

QUENCHED plain carbon steels are hard but have poor ductility. By tempering, the hardness is decreased, the ductility increased, and materials more suitable for engineering applications are obtained. During tempering, the body-centred tetragonal martensite decomposes to give body-centred cubic ferrite and a metastable phase (ε-carbide). On further heating, the stable carbide (cementite) is formed and eventually the ferrite matrix recrystallizes. At this stage the structure is known as sorbite.

If any retained austenite is present after quenching, this also decomposes during tempering to give a carbide and ferrite.

The final stage of tempering is the growth of the ferrite grains. The cementite particles are present at the ferrite grain boundaries and, as the mean particle size increases by resolution of the small particles and growth of the large particles, so the ferrite grains can grow also.

The microstructural changes that occur during the tempering of steel are on such a fine scale that it is only after tempering at $>600°$ C that the structures are clearly resolvable with the optical microscope. It is essential, therefore, to use the electron microscope.

PLATE LXIII

Figures 19.1–19.4

FIG. 19.1. 0·4% Carbon steel, heated at 900° C, tempered for 5 h at 350° C. Etched in 2% nital. The traces of the original martensite grains are still visible but individual carbides are not resolved. × 750.

FIG. 19.2. 0·4% Carbon steel, heated at 900° C, water-quenched and tempered for 100 h at 700° C. Etched in 2% nital. The ferrite matrix has recrystallized and cementite particles are present, chiefly at the grain boundaries. × 1000.

FIG. 19.3. 1·0% Carbon steel, heated at 850° C, water-quenched, and tempered at 200° C for 1 h. Thin foil prepared by electromachining from bulk material, followed by electrolytic thinning. Examined by transmission in the electron microscope. ε-carbide has precipitated as a series of parallel plates perpendicular to the twins formed in the martensite (cf. Fig. 17.5). Electron micrograph. × 75,000.

FIG. 19.4. 1·0% Carbon steel, heated at 850° C, water-quenched, and tempered for 1 h at 350° C. Thin foil prepared by electromachining followed by electrolytic thinning. Examined by transmission in the electron microscope. Cementite has formed within the elongated martensite grains, parallel to the twin interfaces formed during quenching. Electron micrograph. × 20,000.

PLATE LXIII

143

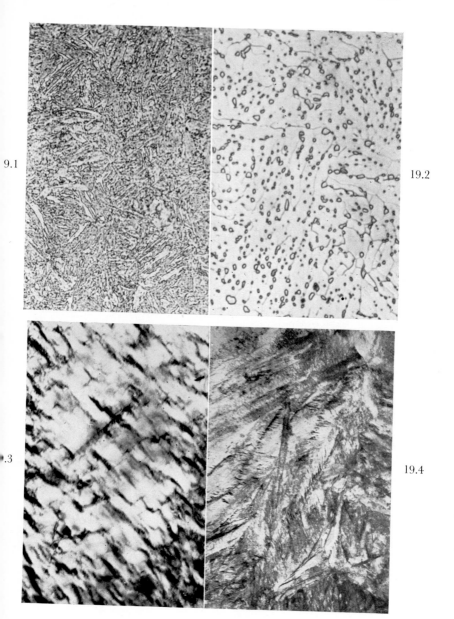

9.1

19.2

.3

19.4

PLATE LXIV

Figures 19.5–19.8

FIG. 19.5. 0·2% Carbon steel, heated at 950° C, water-quenched, and tempered for 1 h at 600° C. Thin foil prepared by electromachining, followed by electrolytic thinning. Examined by transmission in the electron microscope. Equiaxed ferrite grains, relatively free from dislocations, have been nucleated. Elongated ferrite grains having the shape of the original martensite have still not recrystallized and these grains contain many dislocations. Electron micrograph. × 25,000.

FIG. 19.6. 0·3% Carbon steel, heated at 900° C, water-quenched, and tempered for 1 h at 650° C. Etched in 2% nital and a Formvar plastic replica prepared for examination in the electron microscope. The carbides are visible as light-coloured globular particles in a matrix of elongated ferrite grains. Recrystallization of the matrix to give equiaxed ferrite grains has begun in a few places. Electron micrograph. × 5000.

FIG. 19.7. 0·3% Carbon steel, heated at 900° C, water-quenched, and tempered for 10 h at 650° C. Etched in 2% nital and a Formvar plastic replica prepared for examination in the electron microscope. Recrystallization of the ferrite has proceeded to a much greater extent and the carbide particles have grown larger but fewer in number. Electron micrograph. × 5000.

FIG. 19.8. 0·3% Carbon steel, heated at 900° C, water-quenched, and tempered for 50 h at 650° C. Etched in 2% nital and a Formvar plastic replica prepared for examination in the electron microscope. Recrystallization is now complete and resolution and growth of the carbide particles at the grain boundaries has resulted in growth of the equiaxed ferrite grains. Electron micrograph. × 5000.

PLATE LXIV 145

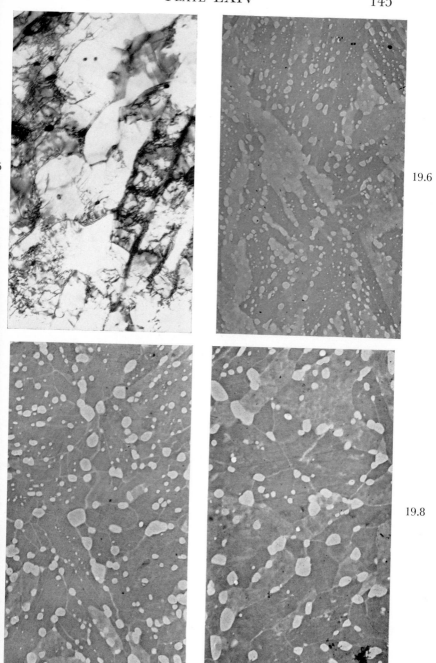

19.6

19.8

PLATE LXV

Figures 19.9–19.11

FIG. 19.9. 0·8% Carbon steel, heated to 850° C, quenched to 250° C, and isothermally transformed at this temperature for 2½ h. Tempered for 1 h at 425° C. Etched in 2% picral. Plastic replica shadowed with chromium and examined in the electron microscope. The cementite particles appear light in colour and are in much the same form as that in which they were originally precipitated within the acicular bainite grains (cf. Fig. 18.14). Electron micrograph. × 7500.

FIG. 19.10. 0·8% Carbon steel, heated to 850° C, quenched to 250° C, and isothermally transformed at temperature for 2½ h. Tempered for 6 h at 425° C. Etched in 2% picral. Plastic replica shadowed with chromium, examined in the electron microscope. There has been spheroidization and growth of the cementite particles but no recrystallization of the matrix ferrite has occurred. Electron micrograph. × 7500.

FIG. 19.11. 1·2% Carbon steel, normalized, and reheated for 50 h at 700° C. Etched in 2% nital. The structure has spheroidized, the primary cementite breaking up into large particles, the pearlite plates into smaller particles. In some pearlite colonies, spheroidization is not complete and elongated lamellæ are still visible. × 750.

PLATE LXV 147

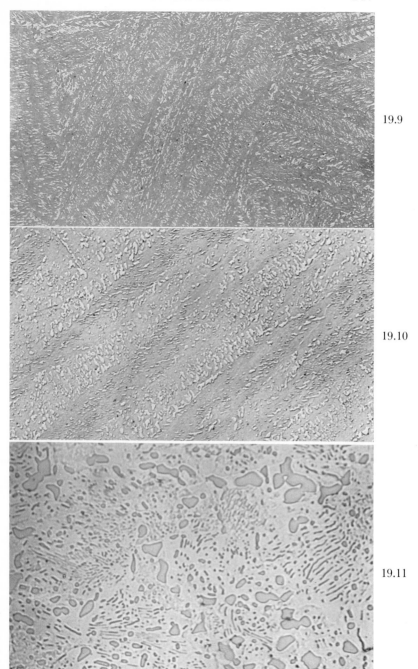

19.9

19.10

19.11

CHAPTER 20

Tempering of Alloy Steels

IF alloying elements are added to a steel, the effects produced depend upon the affinity of the alloying element for carbon. With the addition of elements such as silicon, nickel, and manganese, which have a relatively weak affinity for carbon, the microstructural changes that occur on tempering are almost identical with those found in plain carbon steels. These elements may, however, affect the kinetics of the tempering reactions.

The addition to steel of alloying elements such as chromium, molybdenum, titanium, vanadium, niobium, and tungsten, which have a relatively strong affinity for carbon, may greatly modify the tempering process. The formation of ε-carbide and cementite are retarded and may even be suppressed. Alloy carbides such as Cr_7C_3, Mo_2C, TiC, V_4C_3, NbC, and WC, are then formed at the expense of cementite, and eventually complex carbides of the type $M_{23}C_6$ and M_6C may replace the simple alloy carbides.

On tempering alloy steels containing strong carbide-formers, the hardness may increase, because the alloy carbides are initially precipitated in a very fine coherent dispersion. This phenomenon, which is known as secondary-hardening, is a form of precipitation-hardening.

In chromium–nickel austenitic steels, $M_{23}C_6$ is the most commonly found carbide. This invariably forms at the grain boundaries and leads to weakening and poor corrosion-resistance of the steel. By adding strong carbide-formers such as molybdenum, titanium, or niobium, the properties of these steels may be considerably improved.

PLATE LXVI

Figures 20.1–20.4

FIG. 20.1. 0·2% Carbon, 3% nickel, 1% chromium, 0·5% molybdenum steel, oil-quenched from 830° C. Etched in 2% nital and a carbon-extraction replica prepared for examination in the electron microscope. During cooling, some decomposition of the martensite has occurred, giving small particles of ε-carbide within the grains. Electron micrograph. × 12,500.

FIG. 20.2. Same as Fig. 20.1 but tempered at 600° C for ½ h. Etched in 2% nital and a carbon-extraction replica prepared for examination in the electron microscope. The martensite has decomposed and cementite has been precipitated both at the boundaries of and within the ferrite grains. Electron micrograph. × 12,500.

FIG. 20.3. Same as Fig. 20.1 but tempered at 600° C for 50 h. Etched in 2% nital and a carbon-extraction replica prepared. The ferrite matrix has begun to recrystallize in regions near the prior austenite grain boundaries and equiaxed ferrite grains have formed, with massive cementite particles at their boundaries. Within the unrecrystallized matrix, there are smaller cementite particles. Electron micrograph. × 12,500.

FIG. 20.4. Same as Fig. 20.1 but tempered at 650° C for 100 h. Etched in 2% nital and a carbon-extraction replica prepared. Complete recrystallization of the ferrite has occurred and the cementite has now been replaced by Cr_7C_3, which forms in a characteristic stick-like shape. Electron micrograph. × 12,500.

PLATE LXVI   151

20.1

20.2

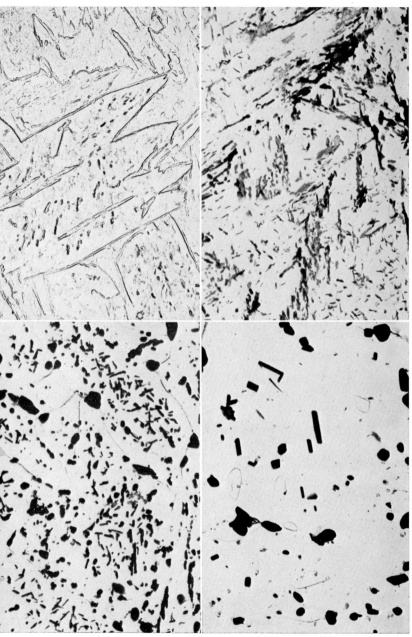

20.3

20.4

PLATE LXVII

Figures 20.5 and 20.6

FIG. 20.5. 0·2% Carbon, 3% chromium, 0·7% molybdenum, 0·7% vanadium, 0·5% tungsten steel, heated at 1150° C for $\frac{1}{2}$ h and air-cooled. Tempered at 750° C for $\frac{1}{2}$ h. Etched in 2% nital and a carbon-extraction replica prepared for examination in the electron microscope. On tempering, V_4C_3 has precipitated within the ferrite in the form of small square plates. Electron micrograph. × 80,000.

FIG. 20.6. 0·2% Carbon, $2\frac{1}{4}$% chromium, 1% molybdenum steel, heated at 960° C for 2 h and then cooled at 300 deg C/h to room temperature. Tempered for 1 h at 670° C. Etched in 2% nital and a carbon-extraction replica prepared for examination in the electron microscope. During cooling from the austenite range, a microstructure of pro-eutectoid ferrite and bainite is formed. On tempering, a fine precipitate of Mo_2C needles forms in both the bainitic and the ferritic regions and as a " fringe " at the ferrite/bainite interface. The large dense particles within the bainitic areas are cementite. Electron micrograph. × 12,500.

PLATE LXVII 153

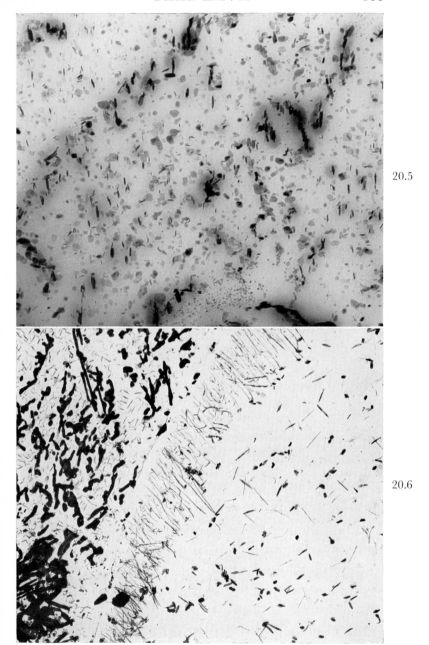

20.5

20.6

PLATE LXVIII

Figures 20.7 and 20.8

FIG. 20.7. 18% Chromium, 8% nickel, 3% molybdenum austenitic stainless steel, heated at 1075° C for 2 h, slowly cooled to 750° C and then maintained at temperature for 20 h. Diamond-polished, etched in 10% bromine–methanol and a carbon-extraction replica then prepared for examination in the electron microscope. A dendritic form of the carbide $M_{23}C_6$ has been precipitated along the austenite grain boundaries. No precipitation is observed at twin boundaries under these conditions of heat-treatment. Electron micrograph. × 10,000.

FIG. 20.8. Same as Fig. 20.7 but heated at 1050° C for 2 h, slowly cooled, and then deformed 5% at room temperature before being annealed at 750° C for 20 h. Diamond-polished, etched in bromine–methanol and a carbon-extraction replica prepared for examination in the electron microscope. The plastic deformation has caused dislocations to interact with the coherent twin boundaries, so making them favoured sites for precipitation of $M_{23}C_6$ in the form of flat triangular particles. Electron micrograph. × 15,000.

PLATE LXVIII 155

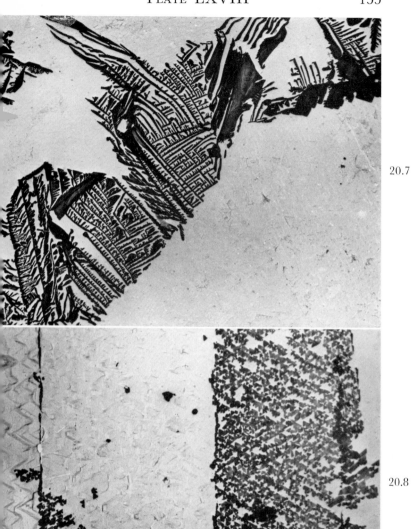

20.7

20.8

CHAPTER 21

Cast Irons

CAST irons are basically alloys of iron and carbon and generally hypo-eutectic, but sometimes hyper-eutectic, in constitution. The carbon can be present either as graphite or cementite. The presence of graphite in cast iron gives a grey fracture and the presence of cementite a white fracture. Irons containing both eutectic graphite and cementite are termed " mottled ".

Grey Cast Irons

In grey irons all the eutectic carbon and hyper-eutectic carbon, if any, is present as graphite, generally in the form of flakes, but the matrix can consist either of ferrite or pearlite, or a mixture of the two. Irons, on solidifying, tend to be grey if they are slowly cooled or have high carbon and silicon contents.

Grey iron is relatively soft and weak but easily machinable. The properties are mainly dependent on the graphite structure, which may be coarse or fine but is generally interconnected within eutectic cells. Phosphorus is present in many grey irons up to $\sim 1 \cdot 4\%$. It appears in the microstructure as a ternary or pseudo-binary eutectic which makes the irons hard and brittle. Flake-graphite grey irons are generally used in the as-cast condition but heat-treatments can be used to alter the matrix structures.

White Cast Irons

All the carbon in white cast irons is present as cementite forming as a constituent of the eutectic, hyper-eutectic, or pearlite. Cast irons, on solidifying, tend to be white if they are rapidly cooled or have low carbon or silicon or high chromium contents. White irons are hard and brittle and are used only where hardness or wear-resistance are important, as in grinding and crushing machinery. White irons are the basic as-cast material for the production of malleable iron.

Malleable Cast Irons

On suitable heat-treatment, the cementite of a white cast iron will decompose and give a final structure of graphite in a matrix of ferrite or ferrite and pearlite. In the blackheart malleable process, the structures are generally uniform throughout. In the whiteheart process, however, heat-treatment is carried out in oxidizing atmospheres and a decarburized surface layer is produced, which is generally fully ferritic and free from any graphite.

In all malleable irons, any graphite is present in the nodular form. The form of the nodules varies according to the manganese and sulphur contents of the iron. In whiteheart malleable iron, the nodules are compact and often spheroidal because of the high sulphur : manganese ratio. In blackheart malleable iron, the nodules are aggregates because of the low sulphur : manganese ratio. Malleable irons are used for some pipe fittings and in the automobile industry.

Nodular or Spheroidal Graphite Irons

Irons that would normally solidify as flake-graphite grey irons can be considerably improved as regards strength and ductility by the addition of magnesium in sufficient quantity to give a residual content of $\sim 0.04\%$. Such irons contain the graphite in nodular form as cast and in many respects are similar to malleable cast irons. Cerium and other alkaline earths exert an effect similar to magnesium. Most of these irons show pearlite structures in the as-cast condition but simple heat-treatment renders the matrix fully ferritic and gives the maximum ductility.

Alloy Cast Irons

Grey irons and nodular irons are generally based on so-called unalloyed materials, in which the main alloying elements are carbon, silicon, manganese, sulphur, and phosphorus. Those irons to which other elements are added deliberately, or in which the regular element content is abnormally high, are known as alloy cast irons. In general, alloying affects the matrix to give special mechanical properties or resistance to chemical attack and high-temperature oxidation.

PLATE LXIX

Figures 21.1–21.4

FIG. 21.1. Grey cast iron (3·1% C, 1·8% Si, 0·15% P). Etched in 4% picral. Graphite flakes and small areas of phosphide eutectic in a matrix of pearlite. × 100.

FIG. 21.2. Grey cast iron (3·2% C, 2·6% Si, 1·2% P). Etched in 4% picral. Graphite flakes are surrounded by a pearlitic matrix. There are extensive areas of phosphide eutectic. × 100.

FIG. 21.3. Phosphide eutectic in grey cast iron. Etched in 4% picral. The Fe_3P–(Fe_3C–Fe) pseudo-binary eutectic is surrounded by pearlite. × 600.

FIG. 21.4. Same area as Fig. 21.3 but etched in Murakami's reagent. The Fe_3P is stained black by this reagent. × 600.

PLATE LXIX 159

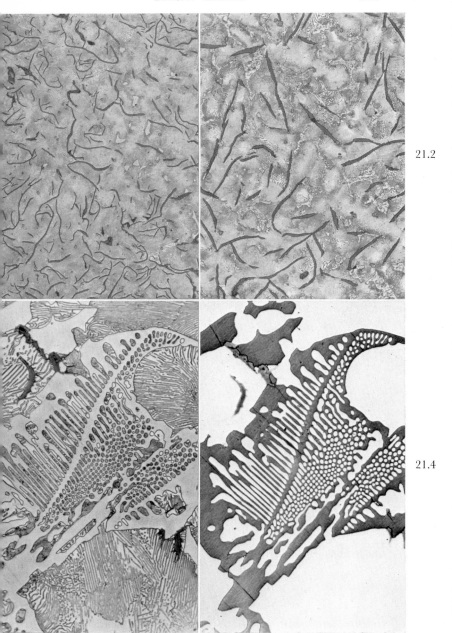

21.2

21.4

Plate LXX

Figures 21.5–21.8

Fig. 21.5. White cast iron (3·2% C, 0·8% Si). Etched in 4% picral. As the composition is hypo-eutectic, dendrites of austenite are formed from the melt. The eutectic (Ledeburite) is composed of austenite and cementite and on cooling to below the eutectoid temperature all the austenite transforms to pearlite. On etching, the pearlite is rapidly attacked and in this micrograph is not resolved as a lamellar structure. Therefore, both transformed primary austenite and eutectic austenite appears as grey regions, while the eutectic cementite is white. × 100.

Fig. 21.6. Blackheart malleable iron (2·5% C, 0·9% Si, 0·4% Mn, 0·09% S). Etched in 5% nital. On casting, the solidified iron is white and, during malleabilizing, graphite rosettes are formed by precipitation from the austenite. On cooling slowly, the remaining austenite decomposes to give graphite, which precipitates on the existing rosettes and leaves a matrix of ferrite. Because of the low sulphur : manganese ratio the graphite forms irregular aggregates. × 100.

Fig. 21.7. Whiteheart malleable iron (3·5% C, 0·5% Si, 0·26% Mn, 0·17% S). Etched in 4% picral. On casting, the solidified iron is white but during reheating in an oxidizing atmosphere the surface layers are decarburized. Therefore, on cooling, the austenite transforms to ferrite but, towards the centre, areas of pearlite and some graphite nodules are found. In thin sections complete decarburization may occur. × 100.

Fig. 21.8. Same specimen as Fig. 21.7 but from the centre of the casting. During reheating, graphite is precipitated from the austenite and in view of the high sulphur : manganese ratio, the nodules are spherical rather than the irregular rosettes shown in Fig. 21.6. On cooling, the remaining austenite, which may be of hypo-eutectoid composition, transforms to ferrite and pearlite. × 100.

PLATE LXX   161

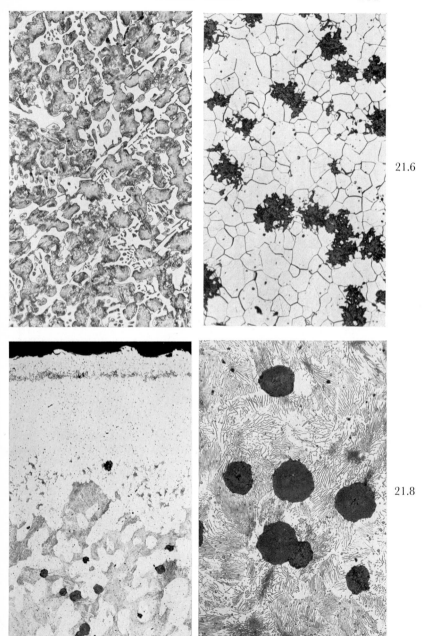

21.6

21.8

PLATE LXXI

Figures 21.9–21.12

FIG. 21.9. Nodular cast iron (3·5% C, 2·0% Si, 0·04% Mg (residual)). As-cast condition. Etched in 4% picral. Spheroids of graphite have formed on cooling and the remaining austenite has transformed to pearlite. × 100.

FIG. 21.10. Nodular cast iron as Fig. 21.9. After solidification, the casting was annealed at 850° C for 8 h, followed by treatment at 690° C for 12 h. Etched in 5% nital. On annealing at 850° C, equilibrium between austenite and graphite is achieved. On cooling to the transformation temperature, more carbon precipitates on the graphite nodules and, with further cooling below the transformation temperature, the austenite decomposes, ferrite is formed, and more carbon (secondary graphite) is precipitated on the original nodules. × 100.

FIG. 21.11. Ni-resist cast iron (2·5% C, 14% Ni, 7% Cu, 7% Si, 0·8% Mn, 1·5% Cr). As-cast condition. Etched in 4% picral. Graphite has precipitated in a flake form on cooling but, with the high nickel content, the matrix has remained austenitic. × 100.

FIG. 21.12. (2% C, 4% Si, 21% Ni, 3% Cr). As-cast condition. Etched in 10% ferric chloride. Fine flake graphite is associated with carbides and there is a matrix of austenite. × 100.

PLATE LXXI   163

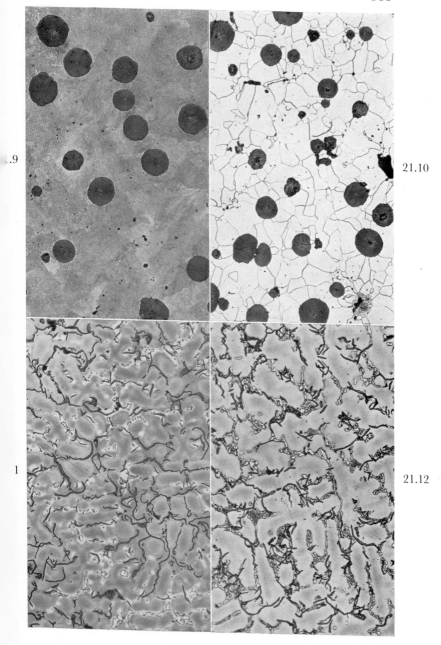

21.10

1

21.12

PLATE LXXII

Figures 21.13–21.15

FIG. 21.13. Ni-hard cast iron (2·5% C, 0·7% Si, 4% Ni, 1·5% Cr). As-cast condition. Etched in 4% picral. With the low silicon content, eutectic carbide has formed. The primary austenite dendrites, containing nickel and chromium, transform to martensite on cooling to room temperature. × 100.

FIG. 21.14. Silal cast iron (2% C, 6% Si, 0·1% Ti). As-cast condition. Etched in 4% picral. The primary dendrites are ferritic, while a eutectic of very fine undercooled graphite and ferrite has formed as an infilling. × 100.

FIG. 21.15. Chromium iron (1·5% C, 2% Si, 31% Cr). As-cast condition. Etched in Vilella's reagent. Primary dendrites of chromium-rich ferrite are formed with an infilling of a chromium carbide–ferrite eutectic. × 100.

PLATE LXXII 165

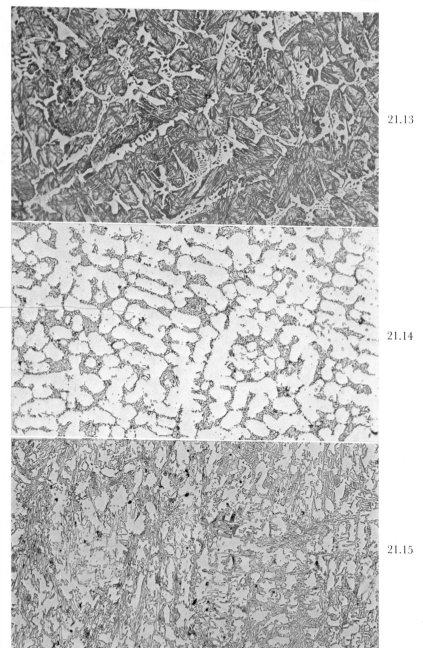

21.13

21.14

21.15

M

CHAPTER 22

Non-Metallic Inclusions

NON-METALLIC inclusions in metals arise from two sources: particles of slag or refractory may become entrapped in the metal while it is still liquid and remain after solidification, (exogenous inclusions); alternatively, during solidification, reactions may occur which lead to the precipitation of non-metallic phases either in the liquid or solid form (indigenous inclusions).

The exogenous inclusions are usually large particles of a complex nature, their exact composition depending upon the type of process and upon the refractories used. Exogenous inclusions are frequently found in welds, as well as in cast materials. Indigenous inclusions may be considered in two groups: those which precipitate as a result of a purification process (e.g. the deoxidation of steel), and those which form as a result of a natural precipitation of impurities from the liquid metal (e.g. sulphides in steel).

If the inclusions precipitate as a liquid phase they will tend to be globular in shape, while those precipitating in the solid state often have a characteristic morphology. In wrought materials, the size, shape, and distribution of the inclusions may be considerably modified. If hot working is carried out at temperatures where the inclusions are plastic, thin elongated particles may be formed. If the inclusions are not plastic during deformation, then fragmentation occurs and this must be accommodated by heterogeneous strain of the surrounding metal.

PLATE LXXIII

Figures 22.1–22.6

FIG. 22.1. Group of FeO inclusions in steel as cast. Note the characteristic spherical form associated with inclusions forming as a liquid phase. × 250.

FIG. 22.2. Group of MnO inclusions in steel as cast. MnO solidifies above the melting point of the steel and therefore the inclusions have a characteristic angular shape. × 1000.

FIG. 22.3. Group of MnO inclusions in rolled steel bar. During rolling, the inclusions have deformed plastically and have also fractured. × 1000.

FIG. 22.4. α-Alumina inclusion in steel as cast. The alumina has a melting point of 2050° C and precipitates as a solid phase during deoxidation of steel. × 1000.

FIG. 22.5. Alumino-silicate inclusions in rolled steel bar. Plastic deformation and fragmentation have occurred during rolling. × 750.

FIG. 22.6. Large globular inclusion of FeO (dendrites) in a matrix of the FeO–2FeO.SiO$_2$ eutectic in steel as cast. × 750.

Plate LXXIII 169

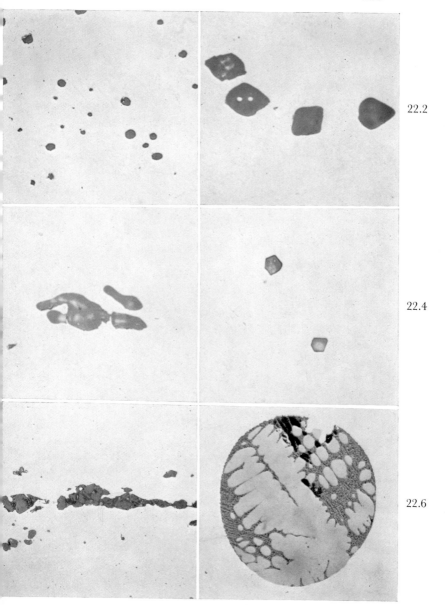

22.2

22.4

22.6

PLATE LXXIV

Figures 22.7–22.12

FIG. 22.7. Group of glassy silicate inclusions in steel as cast. × 2000.

FIG. 22.8. Silicate inclusions in rolled steel bar. At the rolling temperature, the inclusions were plastic and were able to deform plastically within the matrix without fragmentation. × 750.

FIG. 22.9. Duplex oxide/silicate inclusions in rolled steel bar. Both elongation and fragmentation have occurred during rolling. × 750.

FIG. 22.10. Fragmented silicate inclusions in rolled steel bar. Tilting of the fractured blocks has occurred during deformation. This leads to heterogeneous flow, particularly at the corners of the blocks where in many cases voids are left behind. Internal cracks may be nucleated by such inclusions. × 750.

FIG. 22.11. Duplex MnS/FeS inclusion in ingot of forging steel. The manganese sulphide is dark grey, the iron sulphide is light grey. × 250.

FIG. 22.12. Manganese sulphide inclusions in rolled bar of free-cutting steel containing 0·2% sulphur. × 250.

PLATE LXXIV   171

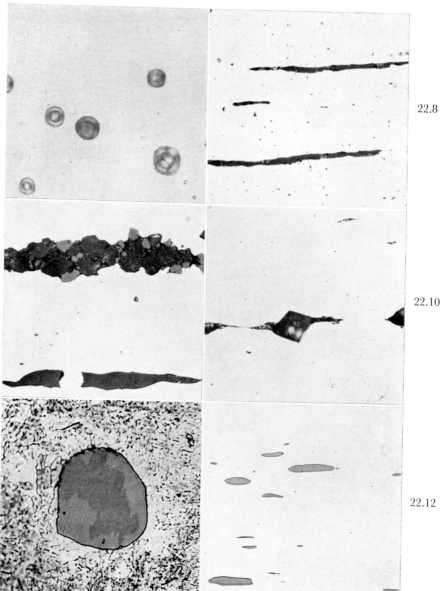

22.8

22.10

22.12

PLATE LXXV

Figures 22.13–22.17

FIG. 22.13. Duplex sulphide/silicate inclusion in rolled bar of free-cutting steel containing 0·2% sulphur. At the rolling temperature, the sulphide (light grey) was ductile, but the silicate (dark grey) shows severe fragmentation. × 250.

FIG. 22.14. Eutectic distribution of MnS in corner section of large steel ingot. On cooling, the eutectic between MnS and austenite is formed, but the austenite transforms on cooling. The occurrence of sulphide in this form makes the steel susceptible to intercrystalline failure. Such structures may also be found in steel overheated during forging. × 750.

FIG. 22.15. α-Ti$_2$O$_3$ in steel as cast. Polarized light. × 1000.

FIG. 22.16. TiN inclusion in rolled steel bar. These inclusions may be readily identified under the optical microscope by their characteristic salmon-pink or yellow colour. × 1000.

FIG. 22.17. Large exogenous inclusion, probably a particle of refractory, in rolled steel bar. × 5.

PLATE LXXV

173

22.13

22.14

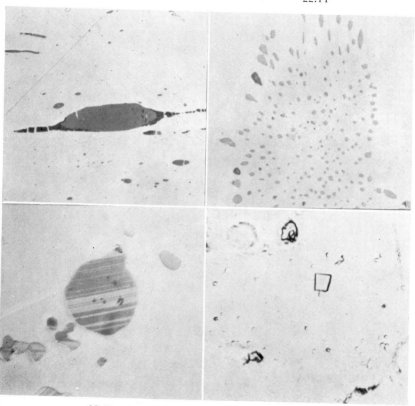

22.15

22.16

22.17

CHAPTER 23

Joining of Metals

IF two pieces of metal were fitted together perfectly on an atomic scale, and if their surfaces were free from oxides and other combined or adsorbed atoms, the pieces would become joined by the atomic bonds formed between them. This is exactly what is made to happen in almost all the methods used for joining metals. In fusion welding, brazing, and soldering, liquid metal is interposed between the pieces to be joined and fluxes are used to remove the surface oxide. While in the liquid state, the metal can take up the shape of the pieces and, on solidification, a continuous joint is the result.

In soldering and brazing, the parent metal is not melted, since filler metals of comparatively low melting points are used. Solder generally consists of low-melting-point lead–tin alloys, the eutectic composition being used when good metal flowability and a short freezing range are required, as, for instance, in joining electrical connections. Alloys of wider freezing range are used when the joint material is to be moulded while pasty, e.g. in the joining of lead pipes. Brazing and silver-soldering alloys have higher melting points, and they are used when greater strength is required or when the joint may be subjected to higher service temperatures than solder would withstand. Solder, silver solder, and brazing alloys have, in general, lower strengths than the materials they are used to join. However, if the layer of joining material is kept very thin and if the surfaces of the pieces being joined have been thoroughly wetted by the liquid metal, the joint strength may exceed the strength of the joining metal itself.

By locally melting the pieces to be joined so as to provide a molten pool between them of substantially the same composition, joint strengths comparable with, or superior to, those of the parent metal can be produced. This is the basis of fusion-welding techniques. In many of them, filler metal is added to the molten pool and protection from the atmosphere is provided either by a shielding gas or by a slag.

The welding method most commonly used in practice is the metal-arc process, in which the filler wire is coated with a thick layer of mineral particles held together by bonding material. The weld is made by striking an electric arc between the joint pieces and the electrode, a molten pool is formed, and the filler wire melts progres-

sively into it. The coating material forms a slag which both pro-
tects the pool and acts as a refining agent.

Alternative techniques of electric-arc welding employ gas shielding, in which the arc is struck either between a consumable filler
wire and the joint or between a non-consumable electrode and the
joint, the filler wire being fed to the pool separately. Such methods
may lead to greater versatility than is possible with the metal-arc
process and permit the welding of more reactive materials. Argon
shielding, either with tungsten electrodes or with consumable electrodes, is particularly suitable for welding light alloys and austenitic
steel sheet. Another advantage of gas-shielded techniques is the
ease with which they can be made semi- or completely automatic.
This gives them greater potential economic advantages, since it can
lead to increased welding speed and greater uniformity of quality.
Two further automatic welding techniques are the submerged-arc
and the electro-slag processes.

Other methods of welding which involve fusion are resistance
welding and flash welding. In the first of these, the pieces to be
welded are pressed together between the electrodes and a heavy
current is passed for a short time, causing melting at the junction
and producing a spot weld. The electrodes may be in the form of
narrow rollers, which rotate and give a series of spot welds, so
forming a seam weld.

In flash welding, the joint pieces are made to come into intermit-
tent contact while a heavy current is passed across the junction.
When the temperature is sufficiently high, an upset force is applied
and the molten and pasty metal is expelled. This method is often
used for butt welding pipe.

It is unnecessary for melting to take place for a weld to be produced. Smiths have been forge welding for centuries. The pieces
are heated to forging temperature and then hammered together;
nowadays fluxing material is usually placed between the joint faces.
Oxide films are broken up and squeezed out and the joint faces
deform to fit each other. In friction welding, the pieces are not
heated externally; one is rotated against the other under a light
load causing intense deformation at the joint and a rise in temperature, then an upset force is applied to produce a weld. This welding
technique is potentially very attractive for making joints between
dissimilar materials, which are troublesome to weld by other methods.

The characteristic microstructural features of a joint are the
molten zone of weld metal, the fusion zone between the weld metal
and the parent material, and the heat-affected zone adjacent to the
fusion zone.

PLATE LXXVI

Figures 23.1–23.3

FIG. 23.1 Brazed T-joint in copper sheet. Etched in saturated alcoholic ferric chloride solution. The etching reagent has revealed the coarse eutectic structure of the brazing alloy. The smooth fillets and lack of porosity are characteristic of a good-quality joint. In a butt joint, the fit-up should be much closer than is shown in the micrograph, but in a T-joint a close fit is not so necessary and, in fact, is difficult to achieve when the sheets are large. × 8.

FIG. 23.2. Butt weld in $\frac{3}{4}$-in.-thick mild-steel plate using the metal-arc covered-electrode process. Etched in 10% nital. The first run of this weld has been made using an electrode of small diameter and the weld was then completed from the other side of the plate with a larger electrode. The cast structure is clearly visible in the larger weld run, while the grain structure of the smaller initial run has been completely refined by the heat generated in making the second run. A broad heat-affected zone is clearly visible. × 4.

FIG. 23.3. Multi-run metal-arc weld in 18% Cr, 12% Ni, 1% Nb austenitic steel plate, using a weld metal of matching composition. Etched in boiling 65% nitric acid. The columnar structure of the weld runs is clearly visible and also its continuity between successive runs. × 5.

PLATE LXXVI   177

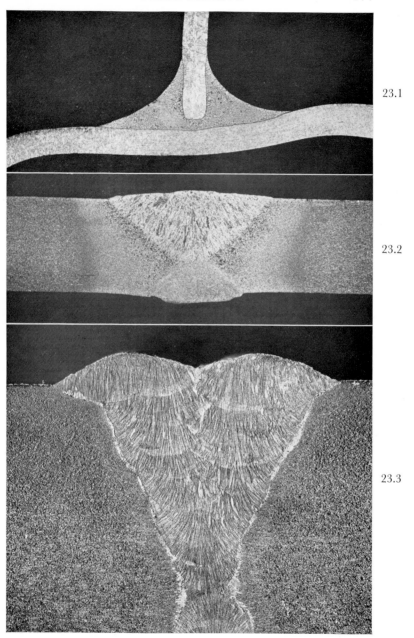

23.1

23.2

23.3

The Microstructure of Metals

PLATE LXXVII

Figures 23.4–23.7

FIG. 23.4. Surface of the solidified weld pool of an argon tungsten-arc spot weld in mild-steel sheet. No metallographic preparation or etching has been carried out. The pool has solidified with a columnar grain structure, each grain being composed of a cell structure. In a normal mild-steel weld metal, the cell structure is difficult to reveal, but it shows up in sharp relief on the surface of the argon-shielded pool. × 600.

FIG. 23.5. Single-run, metal-arc, mild-steel weld metal in the as-deposited condition. Etched in 2% nital. The metal has solidified initially as columnar δ-ferrite grains and subsequently has transformed, first to austenite, and later back to a fine irregular ferrite grain structure with retained austenite and, in some regions carbides, at the ferrite grain boundaries. × 500.

FIG. 23.6. Same as Fig. 23.5 but prepared as a thin foil for examination by transmission in the electron microscope. The structure shows elongated small ferrite grains containing many dislocations. The fine ferrite grain size, coupled with the high dislocation density, accounts for the high strength of mild-steel weld metal in the as-deposited condition. Electron micrograph. × 20,000.

FIG. 23.7. Weld metal (18% Cr, 12% Ni, 1% Nb, austenitic stainless steel) deposited by the metal-arc process. Electrolytically etched in 10% oxalic acid. The grain structure is essentially columnar, but the substructure within the grains shows the deterioration of cells into columnar dendrites as a result of the higher alloy content as compared with mild steel. Randomly oriented dendritic grains are sometimes observed in the centres of austenite weldments, since, during the latter stages of solidification, the temperature gradient in the liquid may have fallen sufficiently to allow separate nucleation ahead of the growth front. × 350.

PLATE LXXVII   179

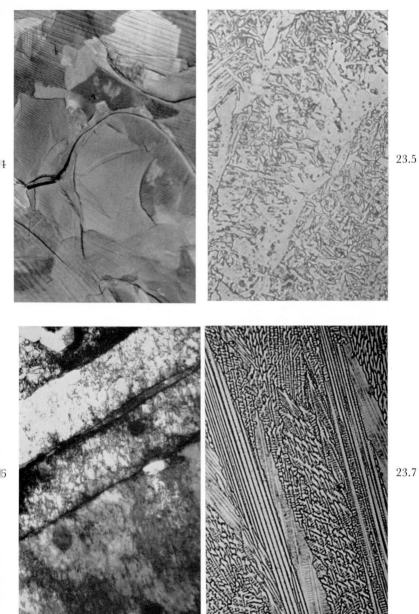

23.5

6

23.7

PLATE LXXVIII

Figures 23.8–23.11

FIG. 23.8. Tungsten inert-gas metal-arc weld (TIG) in commercially pure aluminium. Etched in 10% sodium hydroxide solution. In this process the electric arc is struck between an inert tungsten electrode and the metal to be joined. An argon shield is used for aluminium. The process is capable of a high degree of control and produces a flat, smooth weld bead. It is extensively used for seal welds, welds in thin sheet materials, and corner joints, as illustrated in the micrograph. × 8.

FIG. 23.9. Inert-gas metal-arc weld in $\frac{1}{2}$-in.-thick aluminium–5% magnesium alloy sheet, using argon shielding (MIG process). Etched in 10% sodium hydroxide solution. This process is extensively used for non-ferrous work, since it is easily adaptable to fully automatic procedures and gives a fast rate of deposition. The slight weld-metal porosity would not significantly affect the weld properties. × 3.

FIG. 23.10. Inert-gas metal-arc weld to produce a T-joint in $\frac{1}{2}$-in. mild-steel plate, using CO_2 as the shielding gas. Etched in 5% nital. This process has all the advantages of the argon-shielded (MIG) processes, such as speed of deposition and adaptability to automation, but with the additional advantages of a cheap shielding gas and deep penetration which make it particularly suitable in producing a fully penetrated T-joint of the type illustrated. × 1.

FIG. 23.11. Submerged-arc butt weld in mild-steel plate. Etched in a mixture of equal parts of saturated picral and 15% nital. This welding process is fully automatic, the arc being made between the filler metal and the joint pieces, while powdered flux is fed from a hopper on to the joint just in front of the welding head. With this technique a true electric arc is not formed but resistance heating takes place by the conduction of electricity through the molten slag, followed by heat transfer to the metal; as a result, a deeply penetrating bead is produced. × 1·5.

PLATE LXXVIII   181

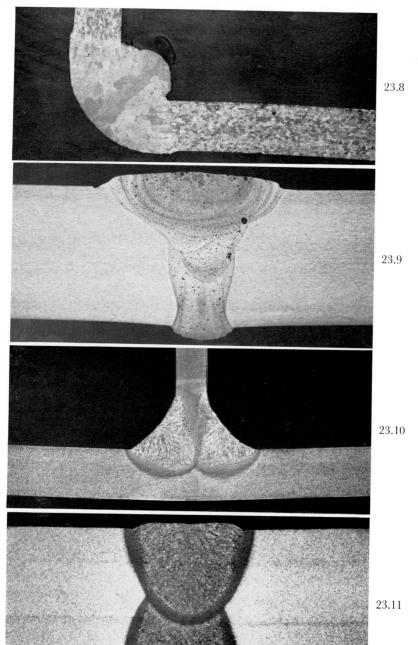

23.8

23.9

23.10

23.11

N

PLATE LXXIX

Figures 23.12 and 23.13

FIG. 23.12. Electro-slag weld in 3-in.-thick mild-steel plate. Etched in a mixture of equal parts of saturated picral and 15% nital. In this process, the plates are prepared with square edges with a vertical gap of ~1 in. between them. Flux is fed into the gap in the form of powder, together with the filler wire. Heat is generated by the conduction of electricity through the molten slag between filler wire and plate, and a large liquid pool is produced. The molten metal is contained in the joint by means of water-cooled copper shoes on each side, which are moved progressively up the joint during welding. Thus, the welded joint is effectively produced by a continuous-casting process. A disadvantage of this process is that a large grain size is obtained both in the weld metal and in the heat-affected zone, which may result in poor mechanical properties. × 1·3.

FIG. 23.13. Same specimen as Fig. 23.12 but normalized after welding. Etched in a mixture of equal parts of saturated picral and 15% nital. Normalizing refines the grain size and gives greatly improved mechanical properties. × 1·3.

PLATE LXXIX 183

23.12

23.13

PLATE LXXX

Figures 23.14–23.17

FIG. 23.14. Resistance spot weld in Nimonic 90 sheet (Cr 20, Co 15, Fe 5, Si 1·5, Ti 2·0, A 11·5, Mo 1·0, C 0·1%, balance nickel). Electrolytically etched in 20 ml hydrofluoric acid, 40 ml glycerol, 340 ml water. This form of welding is extensively used for joining sheet materials. The pieces to be joined are pressed between water-cooled electrodes and a heavy current is passed for a short time, causing local melting. × 10.

FIG. 23.15. Flash butt weld in commercially pure aluminium (99·5%). Etched in ½% hydrofluoric acid. The micrograph shows the extensive " flash " that has been produced by welding and the flow of metal at the joint is clearly visible. In a good flash weld all melted metal should be expelled during the welding process, as in the joint illustrated. × 1.

FIG. 23.16. Friction weld between two pieces of mild steel. Etched in 10% nital. As in the flash-butt-welding process, an extensive "flash" remains around the joint but neither oxide nor other impurities should remain in the joint after welding. × 2.

FIG. 23.17. Electron-beam weld in 18% Cr, 8% Ni austenitic steel. Electrolytically etched in 10% oxalic acid. The process is carried out in an evacuated chamber and is used mainly for reactive metals and small special components. Very narrow, deeply penetrated welds are produced. × 12.

PLATE LXXX 185

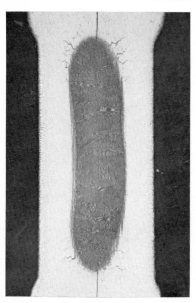

23.15

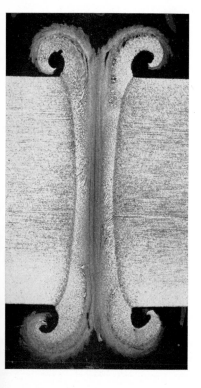

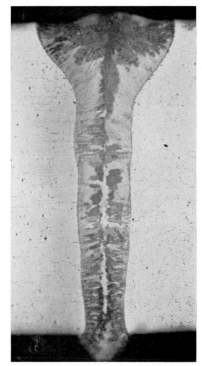

23.17

CHAPTER 24

Surface Treatment of Steels

THE surface treatment of steel components normally involves the modification of the outer layers to provide a hard and/or wear-resisting surface, while retaining a tough, ductile interior. There are two ways of achieving this:

(1) By modification of the chemical composition of the surface layers.

(2) By localized heat-treatment of the surface layers.

Occasionally these two methods are used in conjunction.

The first group comprises a variety of processes and it is convenient to consider them separately, as processes which involve addition of:

(a) Carbon.
(b) Nitrogen.
(c) Carbon and nitrogen.
(d) Sulphur.

(a) In the technological carburizing processes, the steel may be heated in solid, liquid, or gaseous media. It is important to obtain a carburized layer of uniform thickness as rapidly as possible, while avoiding too steep a carbon gradient and the formation of pro-eutectoid cementite networks. To fulfil these criteria, careful control is necessary of the temperature and of the activity of the carburizing medium. The activity may be altered by variation of the chemical composition of the medium and also by the addition of energizers or inhibitors. After carburizing, the components are usually quenched from the austenitic range to give the case the required properties. With gas-carburizing, a direct quench from the carburizing temperature is possible; in pack-carburizing, it is necessary to reheat the steel.

(b) Nitrogen is usually added by heating the steel at temperatures between 500 and 600° C in an atmosphere of pure ammonia, which dissociates when in contact with the surface of the hot metal. Special steels must be used in this process, the common alloying elements being chromium, vanadium, molybdenum, and aluminium. The advantages of the method are that no further heat-treatment is required, the resulting hardness is retained at elevated service temperatures, and components can be nitrided with greater freedom from distortion than is usually possible with carburizing. The disadvantages of the process are that a relatively long nitriding time is required, the steel is expensive, and a soft white layer which is formed on the surface has usually to be removed before the part is put into service.

(c) The principal advantage of the addition of carbon and nitrogen together, by processes such as cyaniding or carbo-nitriding, is that the nitrogen lowers the critical range of the steel. Thus, carbon can be absorbed at temperatures lower than those normally used in carburizing. Nitrogen also increases the hardenability of the surface layers, allowing adequate surface hardening to be obtained at relatively slow cooling rates. By suitably controlling the carburizing atmosphere, the amount of ammonia added, and the temperature, it is possible to obtain a surface layer on mild steel which is martensitic after oil-quenching. The carbo-nitriding process may be used in automatic furnaces and is a cheap technique for hardening small parts.

(d) Sulphidizing is carried out by heating the component either in a solid medium containing a sulphide, such as ferrous sulphide, or in a gaseous atmosphere containing H_2S. The diffusion of sulphur into the surface layer produces sulphides and the process is controlled to obtain maximum penetration while avoiding the formation of sulphide films which might subsequently chip off. The object of the process is to obtain a surface with good bearing properties; the surface hardness is not very much affected.

The surface of both medium-carbon steels and the carburized surfaces of steel components can be hardened by either flame hardening or induction hardening. The only requirements are that decarburization should be absent and that the carbides present in the surface layers should be finely dispersed to ensure that they are taken into solution during the short heating cycle. Flame hardening is carried out using a burner with an oxygen/town's gas or oxygen/propane mixture, which is moved progressively over the component, closely followed by a spray quench. In high-frequency induction hardening the surface heating is obtained from the eddy current induced in the surface layers.

Medium-frequency techniques for through heating are important where rapid heating to high temperatures for short times is necessary. Although the processes described above are all aimed at producing a modification of the surface layers, much heat-treatment is done where it is necessary to avoid altering their composition. In this case control of the furnace atmosphere is important, so that neither carburization nor decarburization occurs. Decarburization can have a very deleterious effect on components such as springs, and the carburization of low-carbon steel components may also lead to trouble in processes to which they are subsequently subjected.

PLATE LXXXI

Figures 24.1–24.6

FIG. 24.1. Mild steel, pack-carburized at 900° C for 2 h in a carburizing " compound " containing 5% Na$_2$CO$_3$ as an energizer. Etched in 2% nital. The surface layers have become sufficiently rich in carbon to exceed the eutectoid composition and on cooling from the carburizing temperature networks of pro-eutectoid cementite are formed and surround pearlite grains. × 250.

FIG. 24.2. Mild steel, pack-carburized at 900° C for 16 h in a " compound " containing 5% Na$_2$CO$_3$ as an energizer. Etched in 2% nital. Increasing the carburizing time has increased the carbon penetration; consequently pro-eutectoid cementite grain-boundary films extend to a greater depth. × 250.

FIG. 24.3. 4¼% nickel, 1% chromium steel, pack-carburized at 900° C for 2 h in a " compound " containing 5% Na$_2$CO$_3$ as an energizer. After carburizing, the specimens were furnace-cooled and then tempered at 550° C to increase the contrast between phases on subsequent etching. Etched in 2% nital. The alloy steel shows much less pro-eutectoid cementite than in Fig. 24.1. The case has a tempered martensitic structure containing some globules of cementite near the surface. × 250.

FIG. 24.4. Same steel, pack-carburized at 900° C for 16 h in a " compound " containing 5% Na$_2$CO$_3$ as an energizer. After carburizing, the specimens were furnace-cooled and then tempered at 550° C to increase the contrast between the phases on subsequent etching. Etched in 2% nital. The increased carburizing time has led to an increase in the austenite grain size and in the amount of pro-eutectoid cementite, some of which is present as a grain-boundary network, but to a much smaller depth than in Fig. 24.2. As in the previous specimen, the structure of the case is tempered martensite. × 250.

FIG. 24.5. Same steel, carburized at 900° C for 2 h in a " compound " containing 1% Na$_2$CO$_3$ as an energizer. After carburizing, the specimen was furnace-cooled and then tempered at 550° C to increase the contrast between the phases on subsequent etching. Etched in 2% nital. This specimen was carburized under the same conditions as those for Fig. 24.3 but with a lower energizer content; consequently the carbon concentration of the case is decreased, and there is no free pro-eutectoid cementite at the surface. × 250.

FIG. 24.6. Same steel, carburized at 900° C for 16 h in a " compound " containing 1% Na$_2$CO$_3$ as an energizer. After carburizing, the specimen was furnace-cooled and then double-tempered at 550° C to increase the contrast between the phases on subsequent etching. Etched in 2% nital. This specimen was carburized under the same conditions as those for Fig. 24.4 but with a lower energizer content. No pro-eutectoid cementite is visible, although the case depth is greater than in Fig. 24.5. × 250.

Plate LXXXI 189

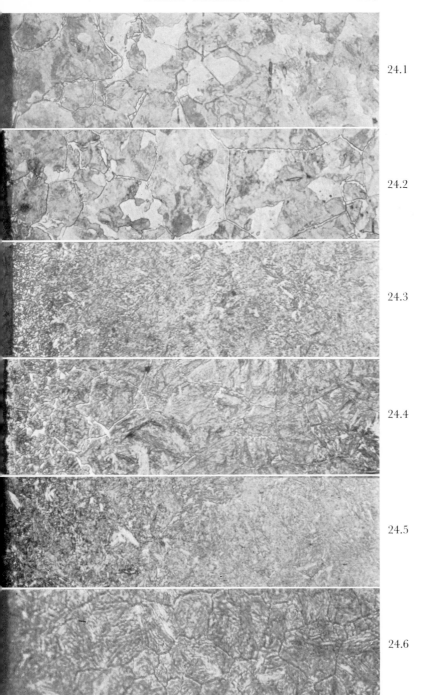

24.1

24.2

24.3

24.4

24.5

24.6

PLATE LXXXII

Figures 24.7–24.10

FIG. 24.7. Nitriding steel (containing 0·3% C, 1·5% Cr, 1% Al, 0·2% Mo). Nitrided in ammonia at 560° C for 24 h (30% dissociation) and air-cooled. Etched in 2% nital. A white layer has been produced on the surface during nitriding and the structure immediately below this is martensitic. × 500.

FIG. 24.8. Same steel, nitrided in ammonia at 560° C for 5 h and then at 580° C for 19 h (50–60% dissociation); then air-cooled. Etched in 2% nital. The shorter time at 560° C, followed by the higher-temperature treatment, has practically eliminated the white surface layer. × 500.

FIG. 24.9. Mild steel, carbo-nitrided at 800° C for 50 min in an atmosphere of town's gas containing 10% NH$_3$, then oil-quenched. Etched in 2% nital. The white surface layer is soft and consists mainly of austenite, the M_s temperature having been drastically lowered by the high concentration of nitrogen at the surface. A black constituent is visible in the austenite in nodular form immediately adjacent to the surface and at the grain boundaries at a greater depth. The composition of this phase is not known. The dark-etching needles within the austenite are of martensite. The amount of retained austenite gradually decreases until a band which is fully martensitic is found to the limit of the case depth. × 250.

FIG. 24.10. Mild steel, carbo-nitrided at 900° C for 20 min in an atmosphere of town's gas containing 10% NH$_3$, then oil-quenched. Etched in 2% nital. Increasing the temperature and shortening the heating time have caused a substantial reduction in the carbon and nitrogen concentration of the case at the surface; consequently the white layer visible in Fig. 24.9, is completely absent. The black intergranular constituent, however, is still plainly visible near the surface. × 250.

PLATE LXXXII   191

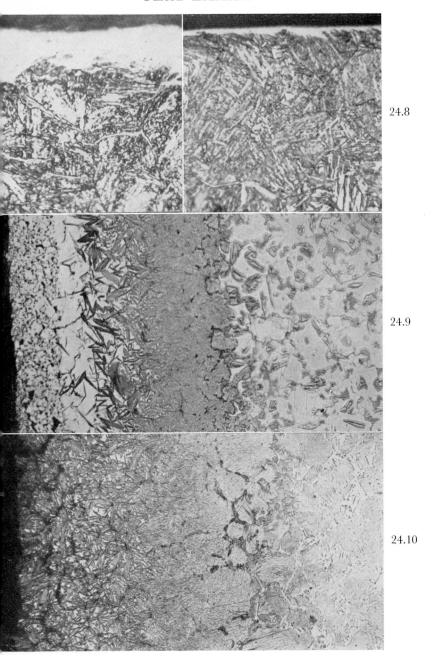

24.8

24.9

24.10

PLATE LXXXIII

Figures 24.11–24.13

FIG. 24.11. Mild steel, carbo-nitrided at 800° C for 50 min in town's gas containing 1% NH_3, then oil-quenched. Etched in 2% nital. By comparison with Fig. 24.9, the decreased amount of ammonia has resulted in less retained austenite in the surface layers and a decrease in the quantity of the black constituent.   × 250.

FIG. 24.12. Mild steel, carbo-nitrided at 900° C for 20 min in an atmosphere of town's gas containing 1% NH_3, then oil-quenched. Etched in 2% nital. The combination of a lower ammonia concentration and a higher carbo-nitriding temperature has resulted in an almost fully martensitic case extending right to the surface of the steel.   × 250.

FIG. 24.13. Sulphidized mild steel. Etched in 2% nital. A layer rich in sulphides has been produced at the surface, while underneath some precipitation at grain boundaries is visible together with needle-like precipitates of iron nitride within the grains.   × 400.

PLATE LXXXIII   193

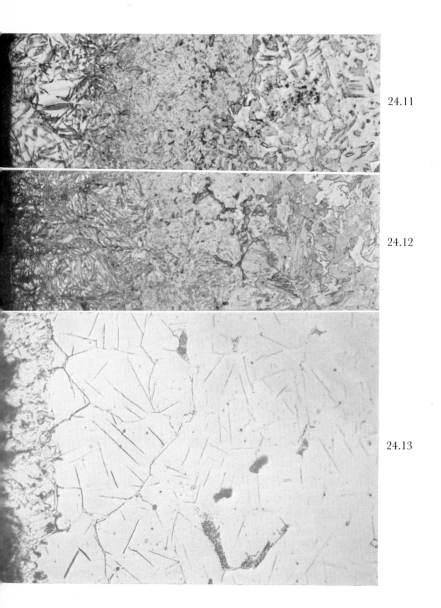

24.11

24.12

24.13

PLATE LXXXIV

Figures 24.14–24.16

FIG. 24.14. Section through the tooth of a flame-hardened fly-wheel gear. Etched in 2% nital and 4% picral. The light-etching hardened structure at the gear tip extends for a distance of ~0·080 in. below the surface, but the boundary is not parallel to the tooth edge. × 5.

FIG. 24.15. High-frequency induction-hardened, medium-carbon steel shaft. Etched in 2% nital and 4% picral. A section has been taken through the shaft to determine the depth of the hardened layer, which appears dark-etching in the photograph and has a thickness of 0·1 in. × 1.

FIG. 24.16. Medium-carbon steel, high-frequency-induction hardened. Etched in 2% nital. The hardened structure is visible as a dark-etching layer adjacent to the surface. The etching characteristics indicate that the layer is not fully martensitic. × 100.

PLATE LXXXIV   195

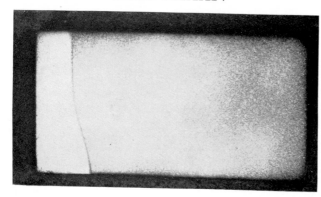

24.14

24.15

24.16

PLATE LXXXV

Figures 24.17–24.20

FIG. 24.17. Rimming steel, heavily cold worked and then annealed for 1 h at 600° C in a furnace. Etched in 2% nital. During annealing, recrystallization and grain growth of the steel have occurred, giving rise to the coarse grain structure in the outer layer and a fine grain structure in the centre of the steel component. × 100.

FIG. 24.18. Rimming steel, heavily cold worked and then annealed for 100 sec at 650° C using medium-frequency induction heating. Etched in 2% nital. The combination of a shorter annealing time with a higher annealing temperature than for Fig. 24.17 has produced a recrystallized structure with a uniform fine grain size throughout. × 100.

FIG. 24.19. Spring steel (containing 0·6% carbon, 1·8% silicon, and 0·8% manganese) which has been heat-treated accidentally in an oxidizing atmosphere. Etched in 2% nital. Decarburization of the surface layer has occurred to produce a light-etching ferritic band adjacent to the surface. × 100.

FIG. 24.20. Free-cutting mild steel (containing 0·12% carbon and 0·7% sulphur) which has been accidentally carburized during annealing. Etched in 2% nital. A layer that is fully pearlitic has been formed adjacent to the surface. This resulted in blistering when attempts were made to plate the component concerned. × 500.

PLATE LXXXV   197

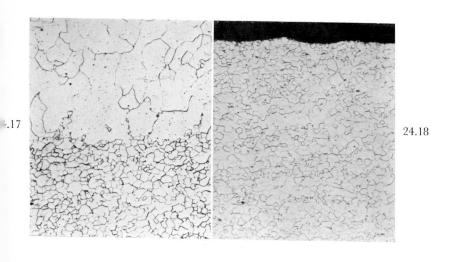

.17   24.18

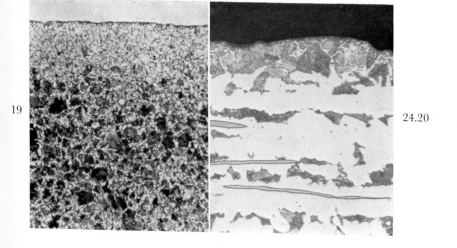

19   24.20

CHAPTER 25

Oxidation of Metal Surfaces

NEARLY all the metals and alloys in common use are unstable in the metallic state at normal temperatures and they tend to revert to the combined state. As the temperature is raised, the rate of oxidation is inclined to increase and this factor frequently limits the temperature range in which a particular metal or alloy can be used. The nature of the oxide film formed on the metal is often the primary factor determining the oxidation rate. To provide good resistance to oxidation, a film must be both continuous and adherent to the surface and must also have a low permeability to the passage of ions and electrons through it. Alloying elements are often added to alloys to improve the oxidation-resistance by modifying the oxide film formed on the surface. Chromium and silicon greatly improve the resistance to oxidation of iron, despite the fact that their affinity for oxygen is greater than that of iron.

The mode of formation of oxide films may change with temperature and with oxidizing conditions. At low temperatures and low oxygen pressures, oxide nodules are formed which then grow into needles and platelets, but eventually, a continuous oxide film is produced. However, a protective slow-growing film may suddenly become non-protective by the preferential growth of nodules and whiskers at a very rapid rate. The factors leading to breakaway growth of this type should be fully understood if the material is to be safely used in practice.

Oxide surface films may confer resistance to room-temperature wet corrosion, as well as to high-temperature oxidation. Aluminium, magnesium, their alloys, and stainless steels are examples of metallic materials which, because of their protective oxide films, need no protection from normal atmospheric corrosion at room temperature. In the case of aluminium, anodic oxidation in acid solution can give a film containing pores which will absorb dyes. The pores can afterwards be sealed and an attractive corrosion-resistant finish is produced on the metal.

Oxidation at elevated temperatures may be prevented by heating in an inert atmosphere but this treatment leads to thermal etching of the metal surface.

PLATE LXXXVI

Figures 25.1 and 25.2

FIG. 25.1. Pure iron, in the form of a single crystal, oxidized at 400° C in air at 1 atm pressure for a period of a few seconds. A carbon replica was prepared from a {100} surface. Before oxidation, the specimen surface was cleaned by reduction in hydrogen. Crystals of oxide have formed on the surface in a definite orientation relationship with the underlying metal. Electron micrograph. × 3000.

FIG. 25.2. Pure iron, in the form of a single-crystal whisker, oxidized at 700° C for 15 min in air at 1 atm pressure. A {100} surface of the specimen was examined directly in the electron microscope. With an increase in the oxidation temperature, preferential growth of oxide needles and platelets occurs. The needles and platelets form from the oxide nodules produced initially on the surface and they grow until they are 5 μm in length. Electron micrograph. × 30,000.

PLATE LXXXVI 201

25.1

25.2

202   *The Microstructure of Metals*

Plate LXXXVII

Figures 25.3–25.5

Fig. 25.3. Oxide scale on pure iron oxidized at 800° C for 10 min in air at 1 atm pressure. Etched in 0·5% hydrochloric acid in alcohol. As the oxidation temperature is increased, continuous layers of scale are produced consisting of haematite (Fe_2O_3) in a very thin layer, magnetite (Fe_3O_4) in a thicker layer, and wüstite (FeO), which forms the thickest layer next to the light-etching metal substrate. The proportion of oxygen in each layer differs, that in the outer layer being greatest and that in the inner layer least. The wüstite layer is non-stoichiometric, being iron-rich near the metal surface and oxygen-rich near the wüstite/magnetite interface. × 1000.

Fig. 25.4. Outer part of the oxide scale on pure iron oxidized at 1000° C in air at 1 atm. Etched in 0·5% hydrochloric acid in alcohol. Raising the oxidizing temperature has increased the thickness of the scale as a whole and of the individual layers. The upper layer is the mounting medium, followed by a thin layer of haematite and a thicker layer of magnetite. According to the iron–oxygen equilibrium diagram, wüstite undergoes eutectoid decomposition to iron and magnetite at 570° C. During the relatively slow cooling from 1000° C, pro-eutectoid magnetite has been precipitated in large particles in the oxygen-rich wüstite of the lower layer. × 1000.

Fig. 25.5. Scale on pure iron oxidized at 800° C for 10 min in air at 1 atm pressure and reheated at 400° C for ½ h. Etched in 0·5% hydrochloric acid in alcohol. During reheating, precipitation of magnetite has occurred both within the wüstite layer and on the metal/scale interface. At the same time, eutectoid decomposition of the wüstite has begun at the wüstite/magnetite interface and the Fe/Fe_3O_4 eutectoid has grown progressively inwards. The magnetite layer found on the metal surface is attributed to preferential eutectoid decomposition there, the iron component being precipitated on the iron surface. The metal layer is at the bottom of the micrograph. × 1000.

Plate LXXXVII   203

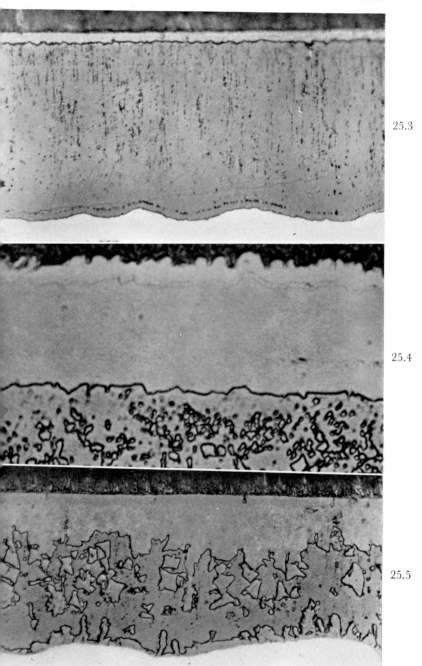

25.3

25.4

25.5

PLATE LXXXVIII

Figures 25.6–25.8

This series illustrates an iron–14·4% chromium alloy, oxidized in air at 1000° C for different periods.   After oxidation, the surface was coated with plastic and a cross-section then prepared and mechanically polished.   On the micrographs, the plastic layer is uppermost.   The weight changes, as a result of oxide formation which occur during heating, are shown schematically in Fig. 25.A. Initially, a protective oxide layer is built up according to curve (OA). Break-through of the film with an increase in the rate of weight change (AB) then occurs.   The film may again become protective, i.e. self-healing, so that the rate of weight change decreases along curve BC.   But in some cases the layer never becomes protective and the curve BD is followed.

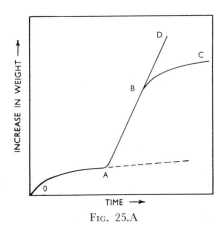

Fig. 25.A

Fig. 25.6. Oxidation time 30 min.   There is a thin protective film, which has broken down in places to give nodules. (Region A, Fig. 25.A). × 500.

Fig. 25.7. After further treatment, some protective film still remains but the nodules have grown much larger and exhibit a stratified structure of light and dark phases with numerous voids.   Internal oxidation of the metal has occurred beneath the nodules but not behind the remains of the protective film. (Region between A and B, Fig. 25.A.)   × 500.

Fig. 25.8. Eventually, a thick oxide scale has been produced with well-defined inner and outer layers, both of which contain voids.   The apparent precipitation in the inner layer of scale near the metal surface is believed to arise from the incorporation of the sub-scale into the rapidly growing scale. (Region between B and C, Fig. 25.A.)

PLATE LXXXVIII 205

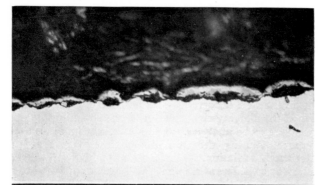

25.6

25.7

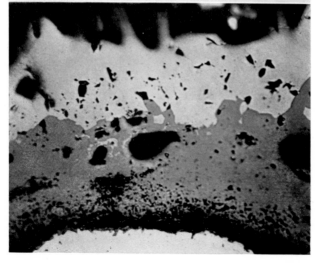

25.8

PLATE LXXXIX

Figures 25.9–25.12

This series illustrates an iron–14·4% chromium alloy, heated in air at 1200° C for 50 h. After oxidation, the oxidized surface was coated with plastic and a cross-section then prepared. During the high-temperature treatment, preferential oxidation of some of the elements in the steel occurred. It is possible to investigate the distribution of the alloying elements in the scale by using the scanning electron-microprobe analyser. The electron beam scans the specimen surface, causing the individual elements present to emit characteristic X-radiation. The X-radiation of given wavelengths, corresponding to different elements, is collected and used to modulate the intensity of the electron beam of an oscilloscope scanning in unison with the electron beam irradiating the specimen. An image is recorded by photographing the fluorescent screen of the oscilloscope. Parts of the surface rich in an element will appear light, while those poor in the element will appear dark.

FIG. 25.9. The scale has a two-layer structure similar to that shown in Fig. 25.8. × 700.

FIG. 25.10. Image of the same area as that shown in Fig. 25.9, but using NiK_α radiation to modulate the intensity of the image. The outer layer and the region of the inner layer adjacent to the metal surface contain very little nickel. Scanning electron micrograph. × 700.

FIG. 25.11. Same area as Fig. 25.10 but using FeK_α radiation to modulate the intensity of the image. The scale immediately adjacent to the metal contains very little iron, but the proportion of iron steadily increases with the distance from the metal surface. Scanning electron micrograph. × 700.

FIG. 25.12. Same area as Fig. 25.10 but using CrK_α radiation to modulate the intensity of the image. The region immediately adjacent to the metal surface is very rich in chromium. The proportion of chromium decreases steadily with increasing distance from the metal/oxide interface, and is very low in the outer oxide layer. Scanning electron micrograph. × 700.

PLATE LXXXIX 207

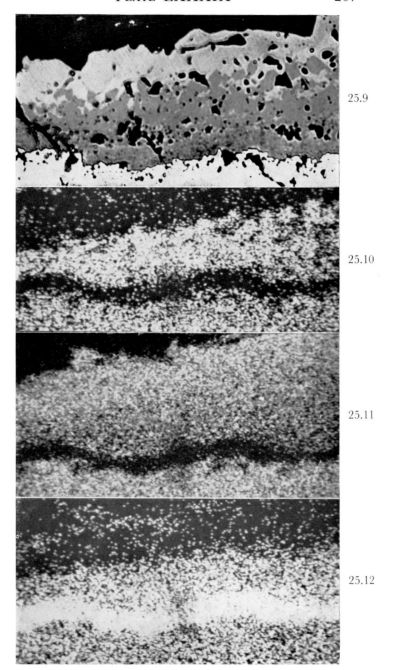

25.9

25.10

25.11

25.12

Plate XC

Figures 25.13–25.15

Fig. 25.13. Pure aluminium, anodized in 10% sulphuric acid to produce an oxide-film thickness of 100 μm. The oxide has been sectioned and then mechanically polished. A Formvar/carbon replica was prepared and examined in the electron microscope. Anodizing in acid solutions gives a porous oxide structure with pores running perpendicularly through the oxide layer. The pore diameter depends upon the anodizing electrolyte, while the pore density increases as the applied voltage increases. The metal layer is at the bottom of the micrograph. Electron micrograph. × 7000.

Fig. 25.14. Similar specimen to Fig. 25.13 but with the section taken obliquely across the oxide layer. The pores show a " rain-drop " pattern. The metal layer is at the bottom of the micrograph. Electron micrograph. × 25,000.

Fig. 25.15. Similar specimen to Fig. 25.13 but the oxide layer has been fractured and the replica has formed around the fractured surface. The pores form perpendicularly to the metal surface but are distributed in regular hexagonal arrays which are visible along the fracture surface. Electron micrograph. × 20,000.

PLATE XC 209

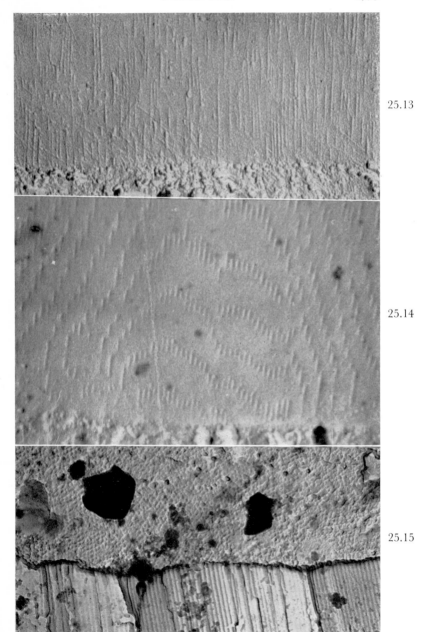

25.13

25.14

25.15

Plate XCI

Figures 25.16–25.19

Fig. 25.16.　0·55% Carbon steel, heated at 1000° C for 2 h in a high vacuum and then slowly cooled back to room temperature. The specimen surface was polished before heating and, during the treatment, thermal etching has occurred giving deep grooves at the austenite boundaries. Twin boundaries are also delineated. The ferrite boundaries developed during cooling are etched, but not as deeply as the austenite boundaries. Some thermal-etch striations have developed within the grains.　× 1100.

Fig. 25.17.　Same specimen as Fig. 25.16, but after treatment the surface was coated with iron by electrodeposition and a section was then prepared perpendicularly to the surface. Etched in 5% picral. The surface acts as a grain boundary and during the $\gamma \rightarrow \alpha$ transformation α is precipitated at the surface in just the same way as at the γ boundaries. The electrodeposit is on the left-hand side.　× 750.

Fig. 25.18.　1·15% Carbon steel, heated at 1000° C for 2 h in a high vacuum, then cooled rapidly. The specimen surface was polished before heating and during treatment thermal etching has occurred. On cooling, pro-eutectoid cementite is precipitated at the free surface (cf. Fig. 25.17). At the surface the strain conditions are relaxed, so that the cementite can decompose to give graphite and ferrite and the associated increase in volume can be tolerated. The graphite nucleation-and-growth rate depends upon the orientation of the underlying cementite; in some grains a complete graphite layer is formed, while in other grains individual graphite nuclei are found.　× 400.

Fig. 25.19.　Single crystal of pure iron. The surface was electropolished, then oxidized in air for a short period; subsequently the oxide was reduced by treatment in hydrogen. A carbon replica was prepared from the reduced surface and examined in the electron microscope. The oxidation and reduction leads to the development of terraces on the specimen surface and a great increase in the specific surface area. Treatments of this type are useful in the preparation of metallic catalysts. Electron micrograph.　× 5000.

25.16

25.17

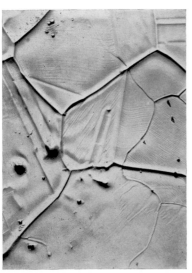

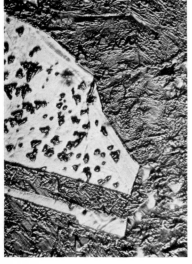

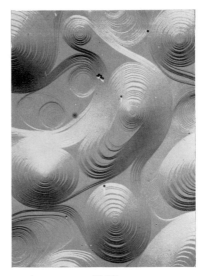

25.18

25.19

Chapter 26

Reactor Metallurgy

At room temperature, α-uranium has an orthorhombic unit cell. On heating, an allotropic change occurs at 660° C to give the β form, which is tetragonal. A further allotropic change to the γ form, which is body-centred cubic, occurs at 770° C.

For fuel elements used in the first British atomic power reactors, uranium was cast into bars, induction heated into the β phase, and quenched by traversing through a water jet. This treatment produces a small grain size and prevents the establishment of significant preferred orientation. Such a structure is required to minimize dimensional changes due to irradiation growth.

In service, nuclear fission occurs, transforming uranium atoms into atoms of lower atomic number with the emission of neutrons. The fission products include xenon and krypton, which tend to accumulate in minute bubbles and cause the uranium to increase in volume. By neutron absorption, elements of higher atomic number, principally plutonium, are also formed.

The displacement of atoms at a fission site results in elongation along the [010] axis of the orthorhombic cell and contraction along the [100] axis, while along the third axis there is no change. At high temperatures, annealing of the irradiation damage occurs and growth is negligible. This change in shape of uranium crystals under irradiation is known as " irradiation growth ", whereas the increase in volume due to fission products is referred to as " swelling ".

The uranium is contained in a sealed magnesium alloy can to prevent oxidation and the escape of fission products. Neutron irradiation does not significantly affect the properties of the can and the only important microstructural change that takes place during irradiation is the development of grain-boundary voids in some cans strained by a slow change in shape of the fuel at temperatures below ∼350° C.

PLATE XCII

Figure 26.1

FIG. 26.1. Unalloyed natural uranium fuel rod, heated to 750° C (β phase) and quenched. Attack-polished in slurry of γ-alumina and 100 vol. hydrogen peroxide, then oxidized in air for 12 h. Examined by polarized light. The section has been taken transversely across the fuel rod and shows fine grains near the rim of the rod.   × 150.

Figures 26.2–26.4

This series illustrates the same material as Fig. 26.1 but irradiated in a Calder Hall reactor to an average burn-up of 4500 Megawatt days/tonne. Attack-polished in slurry of γ-alumina and 100 vol. hydrogen peroxide, then oxidized in air for 12 h. Examined by polarized light. The sections have been taken transversely across the fuel rod.   × 150.

FIG. 26.2. The centre of the rod, which has a larger grain size than the outside and is almost distortion-free.

FIG. 26.3. The region midway between the rim and the centre, where the grains and the twins have been distorted.

FIG. 26.4. The region of the rim, where the structure has been completely distorted during service in the reactor.

PLATE XCII   215

26.1

26.2

6.3

26.4

PLATE XCIII

Figures 26.5–26.8

FIG. 26.5. Unalloyed natural uranium fuel rod heated to 750° C (β phase) and quenched. Electropolished in solution containing 8 parts ethanol, 5 parts glycerol, and 5 parts 85% orthophosphoric acid, then etched in a mixture of equal parts of nitric and acetic acids. A network of uranium–iron and uranium–aluminium precipitates has formed, while there are inclusions of uranium carbide, nitride, and oxide. The carbides are blackened during etching. × 300.

FIG. 26.6. Magnox (0·8% Al, 0·03% Be, balance magnesium), used as a can and irradiated in a Calder Hall reactor. Etched in 5% nital. Intergranular cavities have formed as a result of deformation produced by swelling of the uranium fuel. × 150.

FIG. 26.7. Unalloyed natural uranium in the form of a fuel element irradiated to a burn up of 0·2% of all the atoms at 400–500° C. After removal from the reactor, the fuel element was fractured by impact at room temperature. A two-stage replica (cellulose acetate/carbon) was prepared from the fracture surface and examined in the electron microscope. Intergranular fracture has occurred and fission-product gas bubbles, which have formed at the grain-boundary surfaces, are visible. Electron micrograph. × 13,000.

FIG. 26.8. Uranium–½ at.-% chromium alloy, irradiated to a burn-up of 0·2% of all uranium atoms at 530° C. After removal from the reactor, the specimen was fractured by impact at room temperature. A two-stage replica (cellulose acetate/carbon) was prepared from the fracture surface and examined in the electron microscope. Transgranular cleavage fracture has occurred and fission-product gas bubbles are revealed as they have formed within the grains. The diagonal bands are twins. Electron micrograph. × 26,000.

PLATE XCIII 217

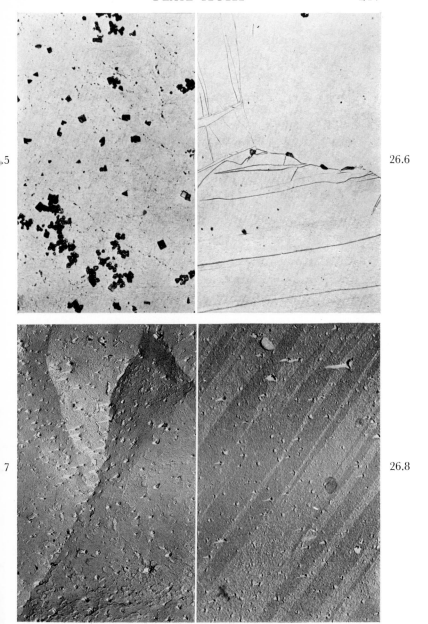

26.6

7

26.8

Chapter 27

Defects Leading to Failures in Service

FAILURE in service can arise from many different causes but these all fall into three main groups, attributable to:

(1) Simple overloading through bad design, incorrect choice of material, incorrect assessment of service conditions, or because of some unexpected alteration in service stress conditions by some unforeseen agency.

(2) Some fault in the material, due to inadequate refining, bad processing, bad fabrication practice, or incorrect heat-treatment.

(3) Incorrect assessment of the effects of environment due to temperature change or corrosion.

When failure does occur, it is important to determine both the type of failure and the factors responsible for it, so that a recurrence can be prevented. The various types of mechanical failure have quite distinctive characteristics which can usually be recognized fairly readily by a visual examination of the fracture surface. These distinctive characteristics are more clearly visible on a microscale and can be examined microscopically by taking a replica of the fracture surface. Unfortunately, however, this is seldom possible with failures occurring in practice, since the fracture surface rapidly becomes corroded or otherwise contaminated.

It is normally desirable to examine a section taken perpendicular to the fracture face, since this may enable the mode of propagation to be determined and also permit the surrounding structure and any subsidiary cracks to be investigated.

Cases of simple plastic collapse due to the application of too great a static load to a structure are relatively rare. However, failure by fatigue is much more common, particularly in welded structures. It may arise either because of the inclusion of a design detail or weld with a poor intrinsic fatigue strength, or because alternating stresses have occurred unexpectedly in a structure not designed to withstand them.

The possibility of brittle fracture arises if a structure:

(a) Is below the ductile/brittle transition temperature of the material composing it.

(b) Contains a notch or other point of stress concentration.

(c) Contains sufficient stored elastic energy due to residual and applied stresses to propagate a brittle crack.

Brittle fractures may be initiated from design details, laminations, notches, cracks associated with welds, or from fatigue cracks. The size of the notch required to start a fracture varies according to the conditions. Except at very low temperatures it must be large enough for the combined effect of residual and applied stresses to produce local tensile stress of yield-point level at the root of the notch.

Corrosion may cause failure through wastage of the metal by general attack, but, more commonly, premature failures are due to intense local attack when the overall corrosion is relatively slight. Examples of this type of attack are stress-corrosion cracking and intercrystalline corrosion. A corrosive environment may also substantially reduce the fatigue strength; even a slightly corrosive environment could easily halve the fatigue limit. This often gives rise to failures in service due to alternating stresses caused by vibration, flexure, &c., which were thought to be negligible when the component was designed.

PLATE XCIV

Figures 27.1–27.24

FIG. 27.1. Fatigue failure experienced in service in a butt weld in austenitic steel sheet. Etched electrolytically in 10% oxalic acid solution. The unfused portion at the centre of the joint has provided a very effective initiation point for the fatigue crack. The fatigue strength of such joints is very poor unless the weld is fully penetrating. × 8.

FIG. 27.2. Cracking in the weld metal of a joint attaching a mild-steel stand pipe to a mild-steel pressure vessel, after heating to a high temperature under high internal pressure. Failure has occurred because the creep ductility of the weld metal was inadequate under the applied temperature and pressure conditions. This vessel was allowed by accident to run at too high a working temperature, so that the failure constitutes a case of overloading in creep. × ⅜.

FIG. 27.3. 0·6% Carbon antimagnetic austenitic steel. Electropolished, electrolytically etched in 10% oxalic acid, and subjected to fatigue. A fatigue crack has initiated from the inclusion situated on the twin boundary. × 500.

FIG. 27.4. Mild-steel weld metal deposited from a metal-arc electrode having a coating with a rutile base on to a cold mild-steel joint. Etched in 2% nitric acid in alcohol. The micrograph shows a small fissure associated with a non-metallic inclusion. Such fissures may be avoided by preheating the joint before the weld metal is deposited. × 1000.

PLATE XCIV   221

27.1

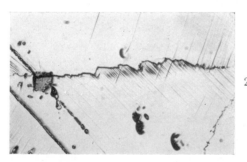

27.2

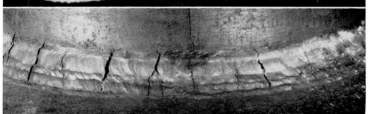

27.3

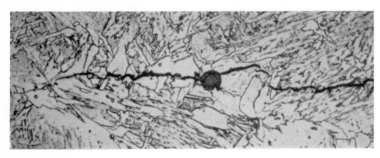

27.4

P

PLATE XCV

Figures 27.5–27.8

Fig. 27.5. Mild-steel specimen taken from a boiler after 20 years in service. Unetched. Graphitization has occurred during service. × 300.

Fig. 27.6. Mild-steel specimen taken from the wall of a pipe. Etched in 5% nital. The pipe wall is badly laminated by two parallel layers of non-metallic inclusions. When this pipe was welded the contraction stresses opened up the laminations near the weld into major cracks. × 60.

Fig. 27.7. Austenitic steel (18% Cr, 12% Ni, 1% Nb), welded with an austenitic electrode. Electrolytically etched in 10% oxalic acid. A transverse section has been taken showing a hot tear in the parent material at the periphery of the weld, produced when regions of local liquation were opened up by the thermal welding stresses. × 150.

Fig. 27.8. Same material as in Fig. 27.7, welded in the same way, then reheated for several hours at 750° C after welding. Electrolytically etched in 10% oxalic acid solution. As in Fig. 27.7, a small hot tear was produced during welding, but, on reheating, an extensive intergranular crack has propagated from this, deep into the heat-affected zone. The cracking arises from a serious loss of ductility of the heat-affected zone due to strain-induced precipitation of carbide, which can result in cracking during the stress relief of welds in thick sections. × 40

Plate XCV 223

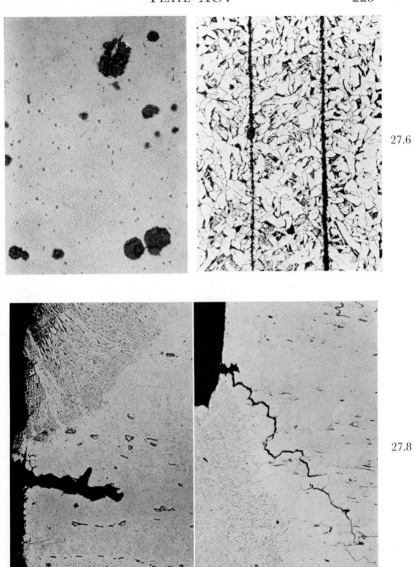

27.6

27.8

PLATE XCVI

Figures 27.9–27.11

FIG. 27.9. Ferritic steel (0·26%C, 1·8%Mn) welded with mild-steel electrodes. Etched in 5% nital. The high cooling rate following welding has produced a martensitic structure in the heat-affected zone. This has cracked spontaneously under the action of residual stresses due to the presence of hydrogen which has diffused into the heat-affected zone from the weld metal. " Hard-zone cracking " of this type is a very serious general problem in welding low-alloy steels. × 3.

FIG. 27.10. Fracture surface of a mild-steel specimen which has failed after heavy plastic deformation, to give a fibrous fracture. Carbon replica. The fracture surface consists entirely of dimples of irregular shape and distribution. Electron micrograph. × 2000.

FIG. 27.11. Fatigue in a high-tensile-steel link plate produced by cycling in tension (44 ± 12·6 tons/in²). Six separate tests were carried out, failure occurring during the sixth through a coupling hole. Unetched. The plate has been photographed end-on to show the fracture face. The fatigue fracture was initiated during the first test and propagated progressively during the remaining five, as shown by the six distinct bands on the fracture surface. × ¾.

PLATE XCVI   225

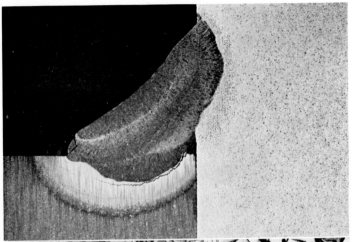

27.9

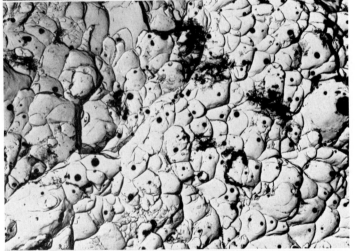

27.10

27.11

PLATE XCVII

Figures 27.12–27.14

FIG. 27.12. Fracture surface of a mild-steel specimen which failed in fatigue. Unetched. Carbon replica. The discontinuous propagation of the fatigue crack is shown by the striations on the fracture surface. Electron micrograph. × 2000.

FIG. 27.13. Fracture surface of a brittle fracture in steel plate just over 2 in. in thickness. Unetched. Distinct chevron markings are evident on the fracture surface, pointing to two separate points of initiation. × $\frac{1}{8}$.

FIG. 27.14. Fracture surface of a mild-steel specimen which has failed by cleavage. Unetched. Carbon replica. The cleavage facets show the presence both of the characteristic river patterns and of " tongues " produced where the fracture path intersects twins. Electron micrograph. × 10,000.

PLATE XCVII   227

27.12

27.13

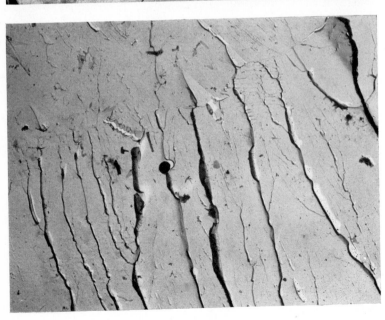

27.14

Plate XCVIII
Figures 27.15 and 27.16

Fig. 27.15. Fracture surface of a mild-steel shaft which has failed partly by fatigue and partly by brittle fracture. Unetched. A fatigue fracture has initiated from a defect at the top of the photograph and then propagated about halfway through the shaft. Ultimate failure occurred by brittle fracture, producing the surface shown in the lower part of the photograph. × 1.

Fig. 27.16. Corrosion-fatigue cracks adjacent to a weld in the wall of a mild-steel tube, resulting from flexure during rotation of the tube in brackish water. Etched in 5% nital. The cracks propagated in a transcrystalline manner and contained corrosion products. The aggressive nature of the environment led to propagation of the cracks under very much smaller fluctuating stresses than those necessary to cause fatigue failure in an atmospheric environment. × 10.

PLATE XCVIII 229

27.15

27.16

PLATE XCIX

Figures 27.17 and 27.18

FIG. 27.17. Austenitic steel (18% Cr, 8% Ni, 0·8% Ti), showing branched transcrystalline cracks caused by stress-corrosion. Etched electrolytically in 10% sulphuric acid in the transpassive range, using a potentiostat.   The failed component was exposed to spray in a boiler system containing water with a very small natural chloride content. The continual splashing and drying led to local concentration of chloride on the surface and eventually caused cracking under the influence of the residual stresses produced during manufacture of the component.   × 500.

FIG. 27.18. Austenitic weld metal used in the component described in Fig. 27.17, showing combined interdendritic and stress-corrosion cracking.   Etched electrolytically in 10% sulphuric acid in the transpassive range, using a potentiostat.   The weld metal shows stress-corrosion cracking, but the interdendritic ferrite has been corroded preferentially, leading to subsidiary interdendritic cracks adjacent to the path of the main cracks.   × 500.

Plate XCIX   231

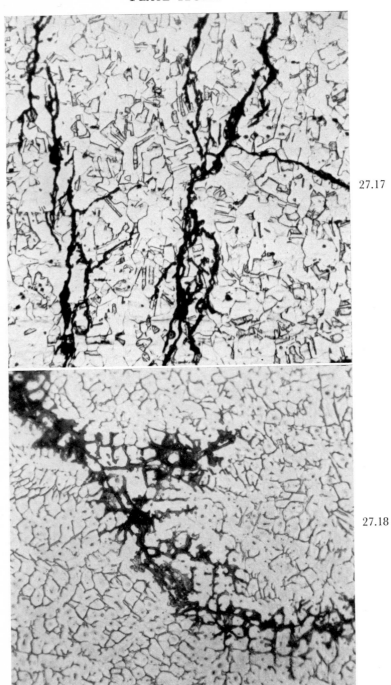

27.17

27.18

232 *The Microstructure of Metals*

Plate C

Figures 27.19–27.21

Fig. 27.19. Mild-steel specimen showing intercrystalline stress-corrosion cracking experienced in the wall of a pipe containing raw town's gas. Etched in 2% nital. This form of cracking occurs as a result of the presence of certain impurities in the gas. It can be prevented by stress-relieving the pipes before they are put into service. × 250.

Fig. 27.20. Austenitic steel (18% Cr, 8% Ni) heated to a high temperature after being brazed. Lightly etched electrolytically in 10% oxalic acid. Intergranular penetration of the stainless steel by the brazing material has occurred while the latter was molten. This caused complete failure of the component in a region just adjacent to that illustrated, by penetration through the entire thickness. × 160.

Fig. 27.21. Austenitic steel (18% Cr, 12% Ni, 1% Nb), welded and then heated for 100 h at 650° C. Exposed to boiling 65% nitric acid, sectioned, and then etched electrolytically in 10% oxalic acid. Localized " knifeline " attack has occurred adjacent to the weld metal. The mode of corrosion is intergranular and is due to the precipitation of the chromium carbides at the austenite grain boundaries. × 50.

PLATE C 233

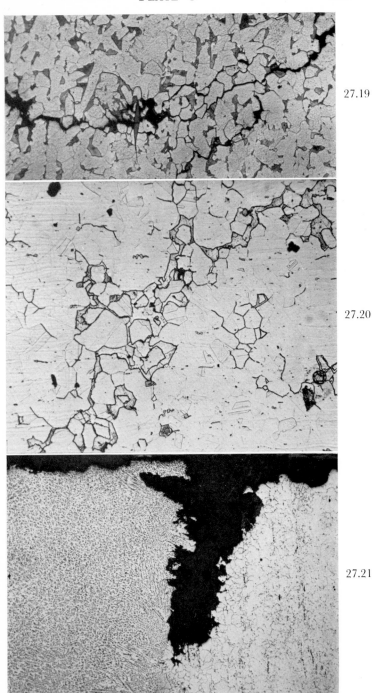

27.19

27.20

27.21

PLATE CI

Figures 27.22–27.26

FIG. 27.22. En 25 steel (0·31% C, 2·53% Ni, 0·61% Cr), heated at 1275° C, air-cooled, reheated to 840° C, oil-quenched, tempered for 1 h at 600° C. Etched electrolytically in saturated aqueous ammonium nitrate solution. The high temperature has led to overheating and as a result the pre-existing austenite grain boundaries are not attacked by the etchant. × 50.

FIG. 27.23. Same steel as Fig. 27.22 but heated at 1400° C and air-cooled, reheated to 840° C, oil-quenched, tempered for 1 h at 600° C. Etched electrolytically in saturated aqueous ammonium nitrate solution. The steel is burnt and partial melting has occurred at the austenitic boundaries. Under these conditions the pre-existing austenite boundaries are dark-etching. × 50.

FIG. 27.24. Same steel as Fig. 27.22 but heated at 1250° C for 30 min, air-cooled, reheated to 840° C, oil-quenched, tempered for 1 h at 600° C. Fractured by impact. The fracture surface shows facets where the fracture path passes around the favourably oriented pre-existing austenite grain boundaries. The fracture is characteristic of incipiently overheated steel. Only a slight decrease in Izod value is apparent after this treatment. × 4.

FIG. 27.25. Same steel as Fig. 27.22 but heated at 1400° C, air-cooled, reheated to 840° C, oil-quenched, tempered for 1 h at 600° C. Fractured by impact. The fracture surface is characteristic of severely overheated or burnt steel. The fracture path is almost completely intercrystalline around the pre-existing austenite grains. Fractures of this type are associated with poor mechanical properties. × 4.

FIG. 27.26. En 111 steel (0·37% C, 1·18% Ni, 0·58% Cr), heated at 1415° C for 7 min and water-quenched. Fractured by impact. Carbon-extraction replica prepared from fracture surface. Fern-shaped α-MnS particles have precipitated on the austenite grain boundaries during burning and this has given rise to intercrystalline weakness. Electron micrograph. × 1500.